Chemistry revision? CGP has the solution...

No doubt about it, GCSE Chemistry is a tough subject. Luckily, this CGP book has everything you'll need, from facts and theory to practical skills — and what's more, there are practice questions on each page to help you sharpen up your exam skills.

How to access your free Online Edition

This book includes a free Online Edition to read on your PC, Mac or tablet.
To access it, just go to **cgpbooks.co.uk/extras** and enter this code...

4018 3477 4557 7675

By the way, this code only works for one person. If somebody else has used this book before you, they might have already claimed the Online Edition.

CGP — still the best! ☺

Our sole aim here at CGP is to produce the highest quality books —
carefully written, immaculately presented and dangerously close to being funny.

Then we work our socks off to get them out to you
— at the cheapest possible prices.

Contents

Topic C6 — Global Challenges

Topic C7 — Practical Skills

Published by CGP.

From original material by Richard Parsons.

Editors: Mary Falkner, Paul Jordin and Sophie Scott
Contributors: Mike Bossart and Paddy Gannon

ISBN: 978 1 78294 567 3

With thanks to Emily Howe and Barrie Crowther for the proofreading.

With thanks to Ana Pungartnik for the copyright research.

Graph to show trend in Atmospheric CO_2 Concentration and global temperature on page 98 based on data by EPICA community members 2004 and Siegenthaler et al 2005.

Printed by Elanders Ltd, Newcastle upon Tyne.
Clipart from Corel®

The Scientific Method

This section <u>isn't</u> about how to 'do' science — but it does show you the way <u>most scientists</u> work.

Scientists Come Up With Hypotheses — Then Test Them

1) Scientists try to <u>explain</u> things. They start by <u>observing</u> something they don't understand.

2) They then come up with a <u>hypothesis</u> — a possible <u>explanation</u> for what they've observed.

3) The next step is to <u>test</u> whether the hypothesis might be <u>right or not</u>. This involves making a <u>prediction</u> based on the hypothesis and testing it by <u>gathering evidence</u> (i.e. <u>data</u>) from <u>investigations</u>. If <u>evidence</u> from <u>experiments</u> backs up a prediction, you're a step closer to figuring out if the hypothesis is true.

About 100 years ago, scientists hypothesised that atoms looked like this.

Several Scientists Will Test a Hypothesis

1) Normally, scientists <u>share</u> their <u>findings</u> in <u>peer-reviewed journals</u>, or at <u>conferences</u>.

2) <u>Peer-review</u> is where <u>other scientists</u> check results and scientific explanations to make sure they're 'scientific' (e.g. that experiments have been done in a sensible way) <u>before</u> they're published. It helps to <u>detect false claims</u>, but it doesn't mean that findings are <u>correct</u> — just that they're not wrong in any <u>obvious</u> way.

3) Once other scientists have found out about a hypothesis, they'll start basing their <u>own predictions</u> on it and carry out their <u>own experiments</u>. They'll also try to <u>reproduce</u> the original experiments to <u>check the results</u> — and if all the experiments in the world <u>back up</u> the <u>hypothesis</u>, then scientists start to think the hypothesis is <u>true</u>.

4) However, if a scientist does an experiment that <u>doesn't fit</u> with the hypothesis (and other scientists can reproduce the results), then the hypothesis may need to be <u>modified</u> or <u>scrapped</u> altogether.

After more evidence was gathered, scientists changed their hypothesis to this.

If All the Evidence Supports a Hypothesis, It's Accepted — For Now

1) <u>Accepted hypotheses</u> are often referred to as <u>theories</u>. Our <u>currently accepted</u> theories are the ones that have survived this 'trial by evidence' — they've been <u>tested many times</u> over the years and <u>survived</u>.

2) However, theories <u>never</u> become totally indisputable <u>fact</u>. If <u>new evidence</u> comes along that <u>can't be explained</u> using the existing theory, then the hypothesising and testing is likely to <u>start all over again</u>.

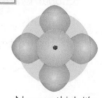

Now we think it's more like this.

Theories Can Involve Different Types of Models

1) A <u>representational model</u> is a <u>simplified description</u> or <u>picture</u> of what's going on in real life. Like all models, it can be used to <u>explain observations</u> and <u>make predictions</u>. E.g. the <u>Bohr model</u> of an atom is a simplified way of showing the arrangement of electrons in an atom (see p.13). It can be used to explain trends down groups in the periodic table.

Scientists test models by carrying out experiments to check that the predictions made by the model happen as expected.

2) <u>Computational models</u> use computers to make <u>simulations</u> of complex real-life processes, such as climate change. They're used when there are a <u>lot</u> of different <u>variables</u> (factors that change) to consider, and because you can easily <u>change their design</u> to take into account <u>new data</u>.

3) All models have <u>limitations</u> on what they can <u>explain</u> or <u>predict</u>. E.g. <u>ball and stick models</u> (a type of spatial model) can be used to show how ions are arranged in an ionic compound. One of their limitations is that they <u>don't show</u> the <u>relative sizes</u> of the ions (see page 19).

I'm off to the zoo to test my hippo-thesis...

The scientific method has developed over time, and many people have helped to develop it. From Aristotle to modern day scientists, lots of people have contributed. And many more are likely to contribute in the future.

Communication & Issues Created by Science

Scientific developments can be great, but they can sometimes raise more questions than they answer...

It's Important to Communicate Scientific Discoveries to the General Public

Some scientific discoveries show that people should change their habits, or they might provide ideas that could be developed into new technology. So scientists need to tell the world about their discoveries.

Technologies are being developed that make use of fullerenes (see p.21-22). These include drug delivery systems for use in medicine. Information about these systems needs to be communicated to doctors so they can make use of them, and to patients, so they can make informed decisions about their treatment.

Scientific Evidence can be Presented in a Biased Way

1) Reports about scientific discoveries in the media (e.g. newspapers or television) aren't peer-reviewed.

2) This means that, even though news stories are often based on data that has been peer-reviewed, the data might be presented in a way that is over-simplified or inaccurate, making it open to misinterpretation.

3) People who want to make a point can sometimes present data in a biased way. (Sometimes without knowing they're doing it.) For example, a scientist might overemphasise a relationship in the data, or a newspaper article might describe details of data supporting an idea, without giving any evidence against it.

Scientific Developments are Great, but they can Raise Issues

Scientific knowledge is increased by doing experiments. And this knowledge leads to scientific developments, e.g. new technologies or new advice. These developments can create issues though. For example:

Economic issues: Society can't always afford to do things scientists recommend (e.g. investing in alternative energy sources) without cutting back elsewhere.

Social issues: Decisions based on scientific evidence affect people — e.g. should fossil fuels be taxed more highly? Would the effect on people's lifestyles be acceptable?

Personal issues: Some decisions will affect individuals. For example, someone might support alternative energy, but object if a wind farm was built next to their house.

Environmental issues: Human activity often affects the natural environment. For example, building a dam to produce electricity will change the local habitat so some species might be displaced. But it will also reduce our need for fossil fuels, so will help to reduce climate change.

Science Can't Answer Every Question — Especially Ethical Ones

1) We don't understand everything. We're always finding out more, but we'll never know all the answers.

2) In order to answer scientific questions, scientists need data to provide evidence for their hypotheses.

3) Some questions can't be answered yet because the data can't currently be collected, or because there's not enough data to support a theory.

4) Eventually, as we get more evidence, we'll answer some of the questions that currently can't be answered, e.g. what the impact of global warming on sea levels will be. But there will always be the "Should we be doing this at all?"-type questions that experiments can't help us to answer...

Think about new drugs which can be taken to boost your 'brain power'.

- Some people think they're good as they could improve concentration or memory. New drugs could let people think in ways beyond the powers of normal brains.

- Other people say they're bad — they could give you an unfair advantage in exams. And people might be pressured into taking them so that they could work more effectively, and for longer hours.

THE GAZETTE
BRAIN-BOOSTING DRUGS MAKE A MOCKERY OF EXAMS

THE POST
GENIUS PILLS TO BECOME THE NEW COFFEE

Tea to milk or milk to tea? — Totally unanswerable by science...

Science can't tell you whether or not you should do something. That's for you and society to decide. But there are tons of questions science might be able to answer, like where life came from and where my superhero socks are.

Risk

By reading this page you are agreeing to the risk of a paper cut or severe drowsiness...

Nothing is Completely Risk-Free

1) A hazard is something that could potentially cause harm.

2) All hazards have a risk attached to them — this is the chance that the hazard will cause harm.

3) The risks of some things seem pretty obvious, or we've known about them for a while, like the risk of causing acid rain by polluting the atmosphere, or of having a car accident when you're travelling in a car.

4) New technology arising from scientific advances can bring new risks, e.g. scientists are unsure whether nanoparticles that are being used in cosmetics and suncream might be harming the cells in our bodies. These risks need to be considered alongside the benefits of the technology, e.g. improved sun protection.

5) You can estimate the size of a risk based on how many times something happens in a big sample (e.g. 100 000 people) over a given period (e.g. a year). For example, you could assess the risk of a driver crashing by recording how many people in a group of 100 000 drivers crashed their cars over a year.

6) To make decisions about activities that involve hazards, we need to take into account the chance of the hazard causing harm, and how serious the consequences would be if it did. If an activity involves a hazard that's very likely to cause harm, with serious consequences if it does, it's considered high risk.

People Make Their Own Decisions About Risk

1) Not all risks have the same consequences, e.g. if you chop veg with a sharp knife you risk cutting your finger, but if you go scuba-diving you risk death. You're much more likely to cut your finger during half an hour of chopping than to die during half an hour of scuba-diving. But most people are happier to accept a higher probability of an accident if the consequences are short-lived and fairly minor.

2) People tend to be more willing to accept a risk if they choose to do something (e.g. go scuba diving), compared to having the risk imposed on them (e.g. having a nuclear power station built next door).

3) People's perception of risk (how risky they think something is) isn't always accurate. They tend to view familiar activities as low-risk and unfamiliar activities as high-risk — even if that's not the case. For example, cycling on roads is often high-risk, but many people are happy to do it because it's a familiar activity. Air travel is actually pretty safe, but a lot of people perceive it as high-risk.

4) People may over-estimate the risk of things with long-term or invisible effects, e.g. ionising radiation.

Investigations Can be Hazardous

1) Hazards from science experiments might include:

- Microorganisms, e.g. some bacteria can make you ill.
- Chemicals, e.g. sulfuric acid can burn your skin and alcohols catch fire easily.
- Fire, e.g. an unattended Bunsen burner is a fire hazard.
- Electricity, e.g. faulty electrical equipment could give you a shock.

Hmm... Where did my bacteria sample go?

2) Part of planning an investigation is making sure that it's safe.

3) You should always make sure that you identify all the hazards that you might encounter. Then you should think of ways of reducing the risks from the hazards you've identified. For example:

- If you're working with sulfuric acid, always wear gloves and safety goggles. This will reduce the risk of the acid coming into contact with your skin and eyes.
- If you're using a Bunsen burner, stand it on a heat proof mat. This will reduce the risk of starting a fire.

You can find out about potential hazards by looking in textbooks, doing some internet research, or asking your teacher.

Not revising — an unacceptable exam hazard...

The world's a dangerous place, but if you can recognise hazards, decide how to reduce their risks, and be happy to accept some risks, you can still have fun. Just maybe don't go skydiving with a great white shark on Friday 13th.

Designing Investigations

Dig out your lab coat and dust down your badly-scratched safety goggles... it's <u>investigation time</u>.

Investigations Produce Evidence to Support or Disprove a Hypothesis

1) Scientists <u>observe</u> things and come up with <u>hypotheses</u> to explain them (see page 2).
   You need to be able to do the same. For example:

   > <u>Observation</u>: People have big feet and spots. <u>Hypothesis</u>: Having big feet causes spots.

2) To <u>determine</u> whether or not a hypothesis is <u>right</u>, you need to do an <u>investigation</u> to gather evidence. To do this, you need to use your hypothesis to make a <u>prediction</u> — something you think <u>will happen</u> that you can test. E.g. people who have bigger feet will have more spots.

3) Investigations are used to see if there are <u>patterns</u> or <u>relationships</u> between <u>two variables</u>, e.g. to see if there's a pattern or relationship between the variables 'number of spots' and 'size of feet'.

Evidence Needs to be Repeatable, Reproducible and Valid

1) <u>Repeatable</u> means that if the <u>same person</u> does an experiment again using the <u>same methods</u> and equipment, they'll get <u>similar results</u>.

2) <u>Reproducible</u> means that if <u>someone else</u> does the experiment, or a <u>different</u> method or piece of equipment is used, the results will still be <u>similar</u>.

Investigations include experiments and studies.

3) If data is <u>repeatable</u> and <u>reproducible</u>, it's <u>reliable</u> and scientists are more likely to <u>have confidence</u> in it.

4) <u>Valid results</u> are both repeatable and reproducible AND they <u>answer the original question</u>. They come from experiments that were designed to be a <u>FAIR TEST</u>...

To Make an Investigation a Fair Test You Have to Control the Variables

1) In a lab experiment, you usually <u>change one variable</u> and <u>measure</u> how it affects <u>another variable</u>.

2) To make it a fair test, <u>everything else</u> that could affect the results should <u>stay the same</u> — otherwise you can't tell if the thing you're changing is causing the results or not.

3) The variable you **CHANGE** is called the **INDEPENDENT** variable.

4) The variable you **MEASURE** when you change the independent variable is the **DEPENDENT** variable.

5) The variables that you **KEEP THE SAME** are called **CONTROL** variables.

> You could find how <u>temperature</u> affects <u>reaction rate</u> by measuring the <u>volume of gas</u> formed over time. The <u>independent variable</u> is the <u>temperature</u>. The <u>dependent variable</u> is the <u>volume of gas</u> produced. <u>Control variables</u> include the <u>concentration</u> and <u>amounts</u> of reactants, the <u>time period</u> you measure, etc.

6) Because you can't always control all the variables, you often need to use a <u>control experiment</u>. This is an experiment that's kept under the <u>same conditions</u> as the rest of the investigation, but <u>doesn't</u> have anything <u>done</u> to it. This is so that you can see what happens when you don't change anything at all.

The Bigger the Sample Size the Better

1) Data based on <u>small samples</u> isn't as good as data based on large samples. A sample should <u>represent</u> the <u>whole population</u> (i.e. it should share as many of the characteristics in the population as possible) — a small sample can't do that as well. It's also harder to spot <u>anomalies</u> if your sample size is too small.

2) The <u>bigger</u> the sample size the <u>better</u>, but scientists have to be <u>realistic</u> when choosing how big. For example, if you were studying the effects of a chemical used to sterilise water on the people drinking it, it'd be great to study <u>everyone</u> who was drinking the water (a huge sample), but it'd take ages and cost a bomb. It's more realistic to study a thousand people, with a mixture of ages, gender, and race.

This is no high street survey — it's a designer investigation...

Not only do you need to be able to plan your own investigations, you should also be able to look at someone else's plan and decide whether or not it needs improving. Those examiners aren't half demanding.

Collecting Data

You've designed the perfect investigation — now it's time to get your hands mucky and collect some data.

Your Data Should be Repeatable, Reproducible, Accurate and Precise

1) To check repeatability you need to repeat the readings and check that the results are similar. You need to repeat each reading at least three times.

2) To make sure your results are reproducible, you can cross check them by taking a second set of readings with another instrument (or a different observer).

Brian's result was a curate.

3) Your data also needs to be ACCURATE. Really accurate results are those that are really close to the true answer. The accuracy of your results usually depends on your method — you need to make sure you're measuring the right thing and that you don't miss anything that should be included in the measurements. E.g. estimating the amount of gas released from a reaction by counting the bubbles isn't very accurate because you might miss some of the bubbles and they might have different volumes. It's more accurate to measure the volume of gas released using a gas syringe (see p.102).

Repeat	Data set 1	Data set 2
1	12	11
2	14	17
3	13	14
Mean	13	14

Data set 1 is more precise than data set 2.

4) Your data also needs to be PRECISE. Precise results are ones where the data is all really close to the mean (average) of your repeated results (i.e. not spread out).

Your Equipment has to be Right for the Job

1) The measuring equipment you use has to be sensitive enough to measure the changes you're looking for. For example, if you need to measure changes of 1 cm^3, you need to use a measuring cylinder or burette that can measure in 1 cm^3 steps — it'd be no good trying with one that only measures 10 cm^3 steps.

2) The smallest change a measuring instrument can detect is called its RESOLUTION. E.g. some mass balances have a resolution of 1 g, some have a resolution of 0.1 g, and some are even more sensitive.

3) Also, equipment needs to be calibrated by measuring a known value. If there's a difference between the measured and known value, you can use this to correct the inaccuracy of the equipment.

You Need to Look out for Errors and Anomalous Results

1) The results of your experiment will always vary a bit because of RANDOM ERRORS — unpredictable differences caused by things like human errors in measuring. The errors when you make a reading from a burette are random. You have to estimate or round the level when it's between two marks — so sometimes your figure will be a bit above the real one, and sometimes it will be a bit below.

2) You can reduce the effect of random errors by taking repeat readings and finding the mean. This will make your results more precise.

3) If a measurement is wrong by the same amount every time, it's called a SYSTEMATIC ERROR. For example, if you measured from the very end of your ruler instead of from the 0 cm mark every time, all your measurements would be a bit small. Repeating the experiment in the exact same way and calculating a mean won't correct a systematic error.

If there's no systematic error, then doing repeats and calculating a mean can make your results more accurate.

4) Just to make things more complicated, if a systematic error is caused by using equipment that isn't zeroed properly, it's called a ZERO ERROR. For example, if a mass balance always reads 1 gram before you put anything on it, all your measurements will be 1 gram too heavy.

5) You can compensate for some systematic errors if you know about them though, e.g. if your mass balance always reads 1 gram before you put anything on it you can subtract 1 gram from all your results.

6) Sometimes you get a result that doesn't fit in with the rest at all. This is called an ANOMALOUS RESULT. You should investigate it and try to work out what happened. If you can work out what happened (e.g. you measured something totally wrong) you can ignore it when processing your results.

Watch what you say to that mass balance — it's very sensitive...

Weirdly, data can be really precise but not very accurate. For example, a fancy piece of lab equipment might give results that are really precise, but if it's not been calibrated properly those results won't be accurate.

Processing and Presenting Data

Processing your data means doing some calculations with it to make it more useful. Once you've done that, you can present your results in a nice chart or graph to help you spot any patterns in your data.

Data Needs to be Organised

1) Tables are dead useful for organising data.

2) When you draw a table, use a ruler and make sure each column has a heading (including the units).

You Might Have to Process Your Data

1) When you've done repeats of an experiment you should always calculate the mean (average). To do this add together all the data values and divide by the total number of values in the sample.

2) You might also need to calculate the range (how spread out the data is). To do this find the largest number and subtract the smallest number from it.

Ignore anomalous results when calculating these.

3) The mode is the most common result in your data set.

4) The median is the 'middle' value. You find it by arranging all your data in numerical order, and then seeing which value's in the middle. If there's two, you take the mean of them.

EXAMPLE: The results of an experiment to find the mass of gas lost from two reactions are shown below. Calculate the mean and the range for the mass of gas lost in each reaction.

Test tube	Repeat 1 (g)	Repeat 2 (g)	Repeat 3 (g)	Mean (g)	Range (g)
A	28	37	32	(28 + 37 + 32) ÷ 3 = 32	37 − 28 = 9
B	47	51	60	(47 + 51 + 60) ÷ 3 = 53	60 − 47 = 13

Round to the Lowest Number of Significant Figures

The first significant figure of a number is the first digit that's not zero. The second and third significant figures come straight after (even if they're zeros). You should be aware of significant figures in calculations.

1) In any calculation, you should round the answer to the lowest number of significant figures (s.f.) given.

2) Remember to write down how many significant figures you've rounded to after your answer.

3) If your calculation has multiple steps, only round the final answer, or it won't be as accurate.

EXAMPLE: The volume of one mole of gas is 24.0 dm³ at room temperature and pressure. How many moles are there in 4.6 dm³ of gas under the same conditions?

No. of moles of gas = 4.6 dm³ ÷ 24.0 dm³ = 0.19166... = 0.19 mol (2 s.f.)

2 s.f.   3 s.f.

Final answer should be rounded to 2 s.f.

If Your Data Comes in Categories, Present It in a Bar Chart

1) If the independent variable is categoric (comes in distinct categories, e.g. alkane chain length, metals) you should use a bar chart to display the data.

2) You also use them if the independent variable is discrete (the data can be counted in chunks, where there's no in-between value, e.g. number of protons is discrete because you can't have half a proton).

3) There are some golden rules you need to follow for drawing bar charts:

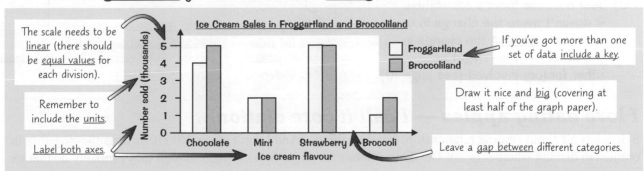

The scale needs to be linear (there should be equal values for each division).

Remember to include the units.

Label both axes.

If you've got more than one set of data include a key.

Draw it nice and big (covering at least half of the graph paper).

Leave a gap between different categories.

Ice Cream Sales in Froggartland and Broccoliland

Number sold (thousands) — Chocolate, Mint, Strawberry, Broccoli — Ice cream flavour

Froggartland / Broccoliland

Working Scientifically

If Your Data is Continuous, Plot a Graph

If both variables are <u>continuous</u> (numerical data that can have any value within a range, e.g. length, volume, temperature) you should use a <u>graph</u> to display the data.

Here are the rules for plotting points on a graph:

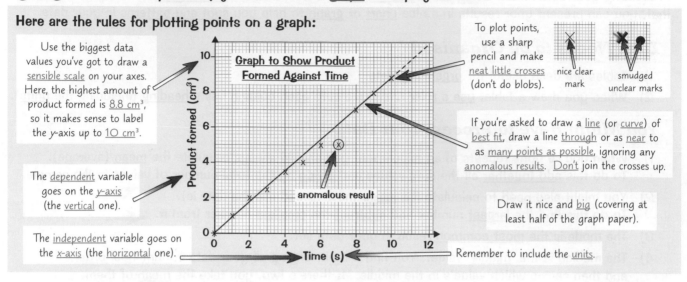

Use the biggest data values you've got to draw a <u>sensible scale</u> on your axes. Here, the highest amount of product formed is <u>8.8 cm³</u>, so it makes sense to label the y-axis up to <u>10 cm³</u>.

The <u>dependent</u> variable goes on the <u>y-axis</u> (the <u>vertical</u> one).

The <u>independent</u> variable goes on the <u>x-axis</u> (the <u>horizontal</u> one).

To plot points, use a sharp pencil and make <u>neat little crosses</u> (don't do blobs). nice clear mark / smudged unclear marks

If you're asked to draw a <u>line</u> (or <u>curve</u>) of <u>best fit</u>, draw a line <u>through</u> or as <u>near</u> to as <u>many points as possible</u>, ignoring any <u>anomalous results</u>. <u>Don't</u> join the crosses up.

Draw it nice and <u>big</u> (covering at least half of the graph paper).

Remember to include the <u>units</u>.

Graphs Can Give You a Lot of Information About Your Data

1) The <u>gradient</u> (slope) of a graph tells you how quickly the <u>dependent variable</u> changes if you change the <u>independent variable</u>.

$$\text{gradient} = \frac{\text{change in } y}{\text{change in } x}$$

This <u>graph</u> shows the <u>volume of gas</u> produced in a reaction against <u>time</u>. The graph is <u>linear</u> (it's a straight line graph), so you can simply calculate the <u>gradient</u> of the line to find out the <u>rate of reaction</u>.

1) To calculate the gradient, pick <u>two points</u> on the line that are easy to read and a <u>good distance</u> apart.

2) <u>Draw a line down</u> from one of the points and a <u>line across</u> from the other to make a <u>triangle</u>. The line drawn down the side of the triangle is the <u>change in y</u> and the line across the bottom is the <u>change in x</u>.

Change in y = 6.8 − 2.0 = 4.8 cm³   Change in x = 5.2 − 1.6 = 3.6 s

$$\text{Rate} = \text{gradient} = \frac{\text{change in } y}{\text{change in } x} = \frac{4.8 \text{ cm}^3}{3.6 \text{ s}} = \underline{1.3 \text{ cm}^3/\text{s}}$$

You can use this method to calculate other rates from a graph, not just the rate of a reaction. Just remember that a rate is how much something changes over time, so x needs to be the time.

The units of the gradient are (units of y)/(units of x). cm³/s can also be written as cm³s⁻¹.

2) To find the <u>gradient of a curve</u> at a <u>certain point</u>, draw a <u>tangent</u> to the curve at that point and then find the <u>gradient of the tangent</u>. See page 70 for details on how to do this.

3) The <u>intercept</u> of a graph is where the line of best fit crosses one of the <u>axes</u>. The <u>x-intercept</u> is where the line of best fit crosses the x-axis and the <u>y-intercept</u> is where it crosses the <u>y-axis</u>.

Graphs Show the Relationship Between Two Variables

1) You can get <u>three</u> types of <u>correlation</u> (relationship) between variables:

2) Just because there's correlation, it doesn't mean the change in one variable is <u>causing</u> the change in the other — there might be <u>other factors</u> involved (see page 10).

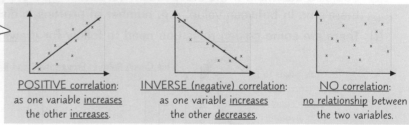

<u>POSITIVE</u> correlation: as one variable <u>increases</u> the other <u>increases</u>.

<u>INVERSE</u> (negative) correlation: as one variable <u>increases</u> the other <u>decreases</u>.

<u>NO</u> correlation: <u>no relationship</u> between the two variables.

I love eating apples — I call it core elation...

Science is all about finding relationships between things. And I don't mean that chemists gather together in corners to discuss whether or not Devini and Sebastian might be a couple... though they probably do that too.

Units and Equations

Graphs and maths skills are all very well, but the numbers don't mean much if you can't get the <u>units</u> right.

S.I. Units Are Used All Round the World

1) It wouldn't be all that useful if I defined volume in terms of <u>bath tubs</u>, you defined it in terms of <u>egg-cups</u> and my pal Sarwat defined it in terms of <u>balloons</u> — we'd never be able to compare our data.

2) To stop this happening, scientists have come up with a set of <u>standard units</u>, called S.I. units, that all scientists use to measure their data. Here are some S.I. units you'll see in chemistry:

Quantity	S.I. Base Unit
mass	kilogram, kg
length	metre, m
time	second, s
amount of a substance	mole, mol

Scaling Prefixes Can Be Used for Large and Small Quantities

1) Quantities come in a huge <u>range</u> of sizes. For example, the volume of a swimming pool might be around 2 000 000 000 cm^3, while the volume of a cup is around 250 cm^3.

2) To make the size of numbers more <u>manageable</u>, larger or smaller units are used. These are the <u>S.I. base unit</u> (e.g. metres) with a <u>prefix</u> in front:

prefix	tera (T)	giga (G)	mega (M)	kilo (k)	deci (d)	centi (c)	milli (m)	micro (μ)	nano (n)
multiple of unit	10^{12}	10^9	1 000 000 (10^6)	1000	0.1	0.01	0.001	0.000001 (10^{-6})	10^{-9}

3) These <u>prefixes</u> tell you <u>how much bigger</u> or <u>smaller</u> a unit is than the base unit. So one <u>kilo</u>metre is <u>one thousand</u> metres.

The conversion factor is the number of times the smaller unit goes into the larger unit.

4) To <u>swap</u> from one unit to another, all you need to know is what number you have to divide or multiply by to get from the original unit to the new unit — this is called the <u>conversion factor</u>.

- To go from a <u>bigger unit</u> (like m) to a <u>smaller unit</u> (like cm), you <u>multiply</u> by the conversion factor.
- To go from a <u>smaller unit</u> (like g) to a <u>bigger unit</u> (like kg), you <u>divide</u> by the conversion factor.

5) Here are some conversions that'll be useful for GCSE chemistry:

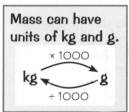

Mass can have units of kg and g.

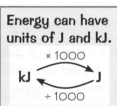

Energy can have units of J and kJ.

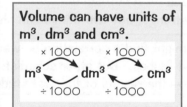

Volume can have units of m^3, dm^3 and cm^3.

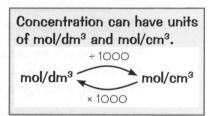

Concentration can have units of mol/dm^3 and mol/cm^3.

Always Check The Values Used in Equations Have the Right Units

1) Formulas and equations show <u>relationships</u> between <u>variables</u>.

2) To <u>rearrange</u> an equation, make sure that whatever you do to <u>one side</u> of the equation you also do to the <u>other side</u>.

You can find the <u>number of moles</u> of something using the equation: moles = mass ÷ molar mass.
You can <u>rearrange</u> this equation to find the <u>mass</u> by <u>multiplying each side</u> by molar mass to give: mass = moles × molar mass.

3) To use a formula, you need to know the values of <u>all but one</u> of the variables. <u>Substitute</u> the values you do know into the formula, and do the calculation to work out the final variable.

4) Always make sure the values you put into an equation or formula have the <u>right units</u>. For example, you might have done a titration experiment to work out the concentration of a solution. The volume of the solution will probably have been measured in cm^3, but the equation to find concentration uses volume in dm^3. So you'll have to <u>convert</u> your volume from cm^3 to dm^3 before you put it into the equation.

5) To make sure your units are <u>correct</u>, it can help to write down the <u>units</u> on each line of your <u>calculation</u>.

I wasn't sure I liked units, but now I'm converted...

It's easy to get in a muddle when converting between units, but there's a handy way to check you've done it right. If you're moving from a smaller unit to a larger unit (e.g. g to kg) the number should get smaller, and vice versa.

Drawing Conclusions

Congratulations — you're nearly at the end of a gruelling investigation, time to <u>draw conclusions</u>.

You Can Only Conclude What the Data Shows and NO MORE

1) Drawing conclusions might seem pretty straightforward — you just <u>look at your data</u> and <u>say what pattern or relationship you see</u> between the dependent and independent variables.

	Catalyst	Rate of reaction (cm³/s)
	A	13.5
	B	19.5
	No catalyst	5.5

The table on the right shows the rate of a reaction in the presence of two <u>different</u> catalysts:

<u>CONCLUSION</u>: Catalyst <u>B</u> makes <u>this reaction</u> go faster than catalyst A.

2) But you've got to be really careful that your conclusion <u>matches the data</u> you've got and <u>doesn't go any further</u>.

> You <u>can't</u> conclude that catalyst B increases the rate of <u>any other reaction</u> more than catalyst A — the results might be completely different.

3) You also need to be able to <u>use your results</u> to <u>justify your conclusion</u> (i.e. back up your conclusion with some specific data).

> The rate of this reaction was <u>6 cm³/s faster</u> using catalyst B compared with catalyst A.

4) When writing a conclusion you need to <u>refer back</u> to the original hypothesis and say whether the data <u>supports it</u> or not:

> The hypothesis for this experiment might have been that catalyst B would make the reaction go <u>quicker</u> than catalyst A. If so, the data <u>supports</u> the hypothesis.

Correlation DOES NOT Mean Cause

If two things are correlated (i.e. there's a relationship between them) it <u>doesn't</u> necessarily mean a change in one variable is <u>causing</u> the change in the other — this is <u>REALLY IMPORTANT</u> — <u>DON'T FORGET IT</u>. There are <u>three possible reasons</u> for a correlation:

1) <u>CHANCE</u>: It might seem strange, but two things can show a correlation purely due to <u>chance</u>.

> For example, one study might find a correlation between people's hair colour and how good they are at frisbee. But other scientists <u>don't</u> get a correlation when they investigate it — the results of the first study are just a <u>fluke</u>.

2) <u>LINKED BY A 3RD VARIABLE</u>: A lot of the time it may <u>look</u> as if a change in one variable is causing a change in the other, but it <u>isn't</u> — a <u>third variable links</u> the two things.

> For example, there's a correlation between <u>water temperature</u> and <u>shark attacks</u>. This isn't because warmer water makes sharks crazy. Instead, they're linked by a third variable — the <u>number of people swimming</u> (more people swim when the water's hotter, and with more people in the water you get more shark attacks).

3) <u>CAUSE</u>: Sometimes a change in one variable does <u>cause</u> a change in the other. You can only conclude that a correlation is due to cause when you've <u>controlled all the variables</u> that could, just could, be affecting the result.

> For example, there's a correlation between <u>smoking</u> and <u>lung cancer</u>. This is because chemicals in tobacco smoke cause lung cancer. This conclusion was only made once <u>other variables</u> (such as age and exposure to other things that cause cancer) had been <u>controlled</u> and shown <u>not</u> to affect people's risk of getting lung cancer.

I conclude that this page is a bit dull...

...although, just because I find it dull doesn't mean that I can conclude it's dull (you might think it's the most interesting thing since that kid got his head stuck in the railings near school). In the exams you could be given a conclusion and asked whether some data supports it — so make sure you understand how far conclusions can go.

Uncertainties and Evaluations

Hurrah! The end of another investigation. Well, now you have to work out all the things you did <u>wrong</u>.

Uncertainty is the Amount of Error Your Measurements Might Have

1) When you <u>repeat</u> a measurement, you often get a <u>slightly different</u> figure each time you do it due to <u>random error</u>. This means that <u>each result</u> has some <u>uncertainty</u> to it.

2) The measurements you make will also have some uncertainty in them due to <u>limits</u> in the <u>resolution</u> of the equipment you use (see page 6).

3) This all means that the <u>mean</u> of a set of results will also have some uncertainty to it. You can calculate the uncertainty of a <u>mean result</u> using the equation:

4) The <u>larger</u> the range, the <u>less precise</u> your results are and the <u>more uncertainty</u> there will be in your results. Uncertainties are shown using the '±' symbol.

The range is the largest value minus the smallest value (see p.7).

$$\text{uncertainty} = \frac{\text{range}}{2}$$

 EXAMPLE:

The table below shows the results of a titration experiment to determine the volume of 0.5 mol/dm³ sodium hydroxide solution needed to neutralise 25 cm³ of a solution of hydrochloric acid with unknown concentration. Calculate the uncertainty of the mean.

Repeat	1	2	3	mean
Volume of sodium hydroxide (cm³)	20.1	19.8	20.0	20.0

1) First work out the range:
Range = 20.1 − 19.8
= 0.300 cm³

2) Use the range to find the uncertainty:
Uncertainty = range ÷ 2 = 0.300 ÷ 2 = 0.150 cm³ So the uncertainty of the mean = 20.0 ± 0.2 cm³

5) Measuring a <u>greater amount</u> of something helps to <u>reduce uncertainty</u>. For example, in a rate of reaction experiment, measuring the amount of product formed over a <u>longer period</u> compared to a shorter period will <u>reduce</u> the <u>percentage uncertainty</u> in your results.

Evaluations — Describe How it Could be Improved

An evaluation is a <u>critical analysis</u> of the whole investigation.

1) You should comment on the <u>method</u> — was it <u>valid</u>? Did you control all the other variables to make it a <u>fair test</u>?

2) Comment on the <u>quality</u> of the <u>results</u> — was there <u>enough evidence</u> to reach a valid <u>conclusion</u>? Were the results <u>repeatable</u>, <u>reproducible</u>, <u>accurate</u> and <u>precise</u>?

3) Were there any <u>anomalous</u> results? If there were <u>none</u> then <u>say so</u>. If there were any, try to <u>explain</u> them — were they caused by <u>errors</u> in measurement? Were there any other <u>variables</u> that could have <u>affected</u> the results? You should comment on the level of <u>uncertainty</u> in your results too.

4) All this analysis will allow you to say how <u>confident</u> you are that your conclusion is <u>right</u>.

5) Then you can suggest any <u>changes</u> to the <u>method</u> that would <u>improve</u> the quality of the results, so that you could have <u>more confidence</u> in your conclusion. For example, you might suggest <u>changing</u> the way you controlled a variable, or <u>increasing</u> the number of <u>measurements</u> you took. Taking more measurements at <u>narrower intervals</u> could give you a <u>more accurate result</u>. For example:

<u>Enzymes</u> have an <u>optimum temperature</u> (a temperature at which they <u>work best</u>). Say you do an experiment to find an enzyme's optimum temperature and take measurements at 10 °C, 20 °C, 30 °C, 40 °C and 50 °C. The results of this experiment tell you the optimum is <u>40 °C</u>. You could then <u>repeat</u> the experiment, taking <u>more measurements around 40 °C</u> to a get a <u>more accurate</u> value for the optimum.

6) You could also make more <u>predictions</u> based on your conclusion, then <u>further experiments</u> could be carried out to test them.

When suggesting improvements to the investigation, always make sure that you say why you think this would make the results better.

Evaluation — next time, I'll make sure I don't burn the lab down...

So there you have it — Working Scientifically. Make sure you know this stuff like the back of your hand. It's not just in the lab that you'll need to know how to work scientifically. You can be asked about it in the exams as well.

States of Matter

All stuff is made of <u>particles</u> (molecules, ions or atoms). The <u>forces</u> between these particles can be weak or strong, depending on whether it's a <u>solid</u>, <u>liquid</u> or a <u>gas</u>. Want to find out more? Then read on...

States of Matter Depend on the Forces Between Particles

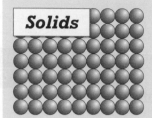

Solids

1) There are <u>strong forces</u> of attraction between particles, which hold them in <u>fixed positions</u> in a very regular <u>lattice arrangement</u>.

2) The particles <u>don't move</u> from their positions, so all solids keep a <u>definite shape</u> and <u>volume</u>, and don't flow like liquids.

3) The particles <u>vibrate</u> about their positions — the <u>hotter</u> the solid becomes, the <u>more</u> they vibrate (causing solids to <u>expand</u> slightly when heated).

4) If you <u>heat</u> the solid (give the particles <u>more energy</u>), eventually the solid will <u>melt</u> and become <u>liquid</u>.

Liquids

1) There is <u>some force</u> of attraction between the particles. They're <u>free</u> to <u>move</u> past each other, but they do tend to <u>stick together</u>.

2) Liquids <u>don't</u> keep a <u>definite shape</u> and will flow to fill the bottom of a container. But they do keep the <u>same volume</u>.

3) The particles are <u>constantly</u> moving with <u>random motion</u>. The <u>hotter</u> the liquid gets, the <u>faster</u> they move. This causes liquids to <u>expand</u> slightly when heated.

4) If you <u>cool</u> a liquid, it will <u>freeze</u> and become <u>solid</u>. If you <u>heat</u> a liquid enough, it <u>evaporates</u> (or <u>boils</u>) and becomes a <u>gas</u>.

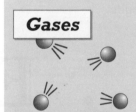

Gases

1) There's next to <u>no force</u> of attraction between the particles — they're <u>free</u> to <u>move</u>. They travel in <u>straight lines</u> and only interact <u>when they collide</u>.

2) Gases <u>don't</u> keep a definite <u>shape</u> or <u>volume</u> and will always <u>fill</u> any container. When particles bounce off the walls of a container, they exert a <u>pressure</u> on the walls.

3) The particles move <u>constantly</u> with <u>random motion</u>. The <u>hotter</u> the gas gets, the <u>faster</u> they move. Gases either <u>expand</u> when heated, or their <u>pressure increases</u>.

4) If you <u>cool</u> a gas, it will <u>condense</u> and become a liquid.

Particle theory is a great <u>model</u> for explaining the three states of matter, but it <u>isn't perfect</u>. In reality, the particles aren't solid and they aren't spheres — they're atoms, ions or molecules. The model doesn't give you any idea of the size of the particles, or the space between them. Also, the model doesn't <u>show</u> any of the <u>forces</u> between the particles, so there's no way of knowing just <u>how strong</u> they are.

Atoms are Rearranged During Chemical Reactions

1) When a substance changes from one state of matter to another (e.g. by melting, boiling, condensing or freezing), it's a <u>physical change</u>. No new substances are made — the original chemicals just <u>change state</u>.

2) Physical changes are pretty easy to undo by <u>heating</u> or <u>cooling</u>. Chemical reactions are a bit different...

3) During a <u>chemical reaction</u>, bonds between atoms break and the atoms <u>change places</u> — the atoms from the substances you <u>start off</u> with (the <u>reactants</u>) rearrange themselves to form <u>different chemicals</u>. These new chemicals are called the <u>products</u>.

4) Compared to physical changes, chemical changes are often <u>hard to reverse</u>.

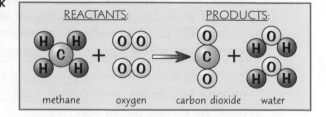

REACTANTS: PRODUCTS:

methane   oxygen   carbon dioxide   water

I felt like changing state, so I moved from Texas to Michigan...

After all this stuff about chemical reactions, let's see how you react to a practice question...

Q1   Describe the forces and the arrangement of particles in: a) solids,   b) gases,   c) liquids.   [9 marks]

The History of the Atom

Atoms are pretty tiny. But what exactly are they like? Scientists have been trying to work it out for years...

The Theory of Atomic Structure Has Changed

Atoms are the tiny particles of matter (stuff that has a mass) which make up everything in the universe...

1) At the start of the 19th century, John Dalton described atoms as solid spheres and said that different spheres made up the different elements.

2) In 1897, J J Thomson concluded from his experiments that atoms weren't solid spheres. His measurements of charge and mass showed that an atom must contain even smaller, negatively charged particles — electrons. The 'solid sphere' idea of atomic structure had to be changed. The new theory was known as the 'plum pudding model'.

electrons | positively charged 'pudding' | delicious pudding

Rutherford Showed that the Plum Pudding Model Was Wrong

1) In 1909, Ernest Rutherford and his students, Hans Geiger and Ernest Marsden, conducted the famous gold foil experiment. They fired positively charged alpha particles at an extremely thin sheet of gold.

2) From the plum pudding model, they were expecting the particles to pass straight through the sheet or be slightly deflected at most. This was because the positive charge of each atom was thought to be very spread out through the 'pudding' of the atom. But, whilst most of the particles did go straight through the gold sheet, some were deflected more than expected, and a small number were deflected backwards. So the plum pudding model couldn't be right.

3) Rutherford came up with the theory of the nuclear atom to explain this new evidence. In this, there's a tiny, positively charged nucleus at the centre, surrounded by a 'cloud' of negative electrons — most of the atom's empty space.

A few particles are deflected backwards by the nucleus. | Most of the particles pass through empty space.

The Refined Bohr Model Explains a Lot

1) Scientists realised that electrons in a 'cloud' around the nucleus of an atom, as Rutherford described, would be attracted to the nucleus, causing the atom to collapse. Niels Bohr proposed a new model of the atom where all the electrons were contained in shells.

nucleus | shells | electrons

2) Bohr suggested that electrons can only exist in fixed orbits, or shells, and not anywhere in between. Each shell has a fixed energy.

3) Bohr's theory of atomic structure was supported by many experiments and it helped to explain lots of other scientists' observations at the time. It was pretty close to our currently accepted version of the atom (see next page).

Scientific Theories Have to be Backed Up by Evidence

1) So, our current model of the atom is different to what people thought the atom looked like in the past. These different ideas were accepted because they fitted the evidence available at the time.

2) As scientists did more experiments, new evidence was found and our theory of the structure of the atom was modified to fit it. This is nearly always the way scientific knowledge develops — new evidence prompts people to come up with new, improved ideas. These ideas can be used to make predictions which, if proved correct, are a pretty good indication that the ideas are right.

3) Scientists also put their ideas and research up for peer-review. This means everyone gets a chance to see the new ideas, check for errors and then other scientists can use it to help develop their own work.

I love a good model — Kate Moss is my personal favourite...

This is a great example of how science works. Scientists working together to find evidence. Lovely.

Q1   Describe how the gold foil experiment disproved the plum pudding model of the atom.   [3 marks]

Q2   Draw and label a diagram to show the Bohr model of the atom.   [2 marks]

The Atom

There are quite a few <u>different</u> (and equally useful) <u>modern</u> models of the atom — but chemists tend to like this model best. You can use it to explain loads of chemistry... which is nice. Well, here goes...

The Atom is Made Up of Protons, Neutrons and Electrons

The atom is made up of three <u>subatomic particles</u> — protons, neutrons and electrons.

- <u>Protons</u> are <u>heavy</u> and <u>positively charged</u>.
- <u>Neutrons</u> are <u>heavy</u> and <u>neutral</u>.
- <u>Electrons</u> have <u>hardly any mass</u> and are <u>negatively charged</u>.

Particle	Relative Mass	Relative Charge
Proton	1	+1
Neutron	1	0
Electron	0.0005	–1

Relative mass (measured in atomic mass units) measures mass on a scale where the mass of a proton or neutron is 1.

In reality, protons and neutrons are still teeny tiny. They're just heavy compared to electrons.

The Nucleus

1) The nucleus is in the <u>middle</u> of the atom.

2) It contains <u>protons</u> and <u>neutrons</u>.

3) It has a <u>positive charge</u> because of the protons.

4) Almost the <u>whole</u> mass of the atom (between about 10^{-23} g and 10^{-21} g) is <u>concentrated</u> in the nucleus.

5) Compared to the overall size of the atom, the nucleus is <u>tiny</u> (the nucleus has a radius of between about 10^{-15} m and 10^{-14} m).

The Electrons

1) Electrons move <u>around</u> the nucleus in electron <u>shells</u> (or orbitals).

2) They're <u>negatively charged</u>.

3) They're <u>tiny</u>, but their orbitals cover <u>a lot of space</u>.

4) The <u>volume</u> of their orbitals determines the size of the atom — atoms have a radius (known as the atomic radius) of about 10^{-10} m.

5) Electrons have virtually <u>no</u> mass — it's often taken as zero.

Houston, we're in orbit.

Atoms are really tiny, don't forget. They're too small to see, even with a very high power microscope.

Molecules Form When Atoms Bond Together

1) <u>Molecules</u> are made up of two or more atoms.

2) Molecules can be made of the <u>same element</u> (e.g. hydrogen), or <u>different elements</u> (e.g. ammonia).

3) Simple molecules (see page 20), like atoms, are pretty tiny. The <u>bonds</u> that form between these molecules are generally a similar length to the atomic radius — <u>about 10^{-10} m</u>.

4) <u>Nanoparticles</u> (see page 22) are a bit bigger than simple molecules. They're typically made of around 100 atoms and range from <u>1 nm</u> to <u>100 nm</u> in size.

hydrogen molecule

ammonia molecule

1 nanometer = 10^{-9} metres.

Don't trust atoms — they make up everything...

You need to learn what's in that table with the relative masses and charges of the different parts of the atom. Try remembering **P**rotons are **P**ositive, **N**eutrons are **N**eutral and **E**lectrons are **E**... Never mind.

Q1   What is the charge on: a) a proton,   b) a neutron,   c) an electron?   [1 mark]

Q2   Where is most of the mass of an atom to be found?   [1 mark]

Q3   Put the following things in order of size, starting with the smallest: atomic radius, nuclear radius, nanoparticle, simple molecule (e.g. Cl_2).   [2 marks]

Atoms, Ions and Isotopes

As if <u>atoms</u> weren't fiddly enough, time to meet those pesky <u>ions</u>. Oh, and don't get me started on <u>isotopes</u>...

Atomic Number and Mass Number Describe an Atom

These two numbers tell you how many of each kind of particle an atom has.

In some notations and periodic tables (like the one on the data sheet in the exam), these numbers are the other way round. Just remember the bigger one is the mass number.

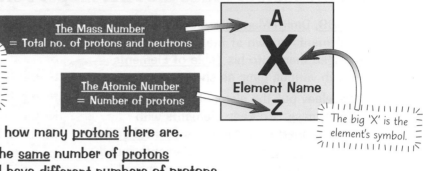

The Mass Number = Total no. of protons and neutrons

The Atomic Number = Number of protons

A
X
Z
Element Name

The big 'X' is the element's symbol.

1) The <u>atomic (proton) number</u> tells you how many <u>protons</u> there are.

2) Atoms of the <u>same</u> element all have the <u>same</u> number of <u>protons</u>
    — so atoms of <u>different</u> elements will have <u>different</u> numbers of protons.

3) To get the number of <u>neutrons</u>, just subtract the <u>atomic number</u> from the <u>mass number</u>.

4) The <u>mass (nucleon) number</u> is always the <u>biggest</u> number. On a periodic table the mass number is actually the <u>relative atomic mass</u> (see page 31).

5) Neutral atoms have <u>no charge</u> overall (unlike ions, see below).
    This is because they have the <u>same number</u> of <u>protons</u> as <u>electrons</u>. The charge on the electrons is the same size as the charge on the protons, but opposite — so the charges cancel out.
    So, the number of electrons in a neutral atom is also <u>equal</u> to the <u>atomic number</u>.

Ions have Different Numbers of Protons and Electrons

1) Ions form when atoms (or groups of atoms) <u>gain</u> or <u>lose electrons</u> (see page 18 for more).

2) <u>Negative ions</u> form when atoms <u>gain electrons</u> — they have more electrons than protons.
    <u>Positive ions</u> form when atoms <u>lose electrons</u> — they have more protons than electrons.

> - F^- — there's a <u>single negative charge</u>, so there must be one more electron than protons.
>   F has an atomic number of 9, so has 9 protons. So F^- must have 9 + 1 = <u>10 electrons</u>.
> - Fe^{2+} — there's a <u>2+ charge</u>, so there must be two more protons than electrons.
>   Fe has an atomic number of 26, so has 26 protons. So Fe^{2+} must have 26 − 2 = <u>24 electrons</u>.

Isotopes are the Same Except for the Number of Neutrons

> Isotopes are different forms of the same element, which have the same number of protons but a different number of neutrons.

1) Isotopes have the <u>same atomic number</u> but <u>different mass numbers</u>.

2) If they had <u>different</u> atomic numbers, they'd be <u>different</u> elements altogether.

3) A famous example is the two main isotopes of carbon.

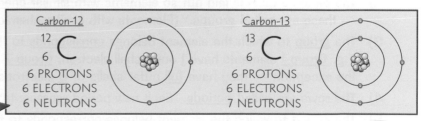

Carbon-12
$^{12}_{6}C$
6 PROTONS
6 ELECTRONS
6 NEUTRONS

Carbon-13
$^{13}_{6}C$
6 PROTONS
6 ELECTRONS
7 NEUTRONS

Na⁺ was positive that he'd misplaced one of his electrons...

There's a smattering of maths here, but it's just some adding and subtracting, so don't worry too much.

Q1 Work out the number of neutrons in the following atoms: a) $^{16}_{8}O$, b) $^{40}_{20}Ca$, c) $^{127}_{53}I$. [3 marks]

Q2 a) Chlorine has an atomic number of 17. It exists naturally with 2 isotopes, chlorine-35 and chlorine-37. Work out how many neutrons, protons and electrons are in each isotope. [2 marks]

    b) Chlorine tends to react by forming Cl^- ions. How many electrons are in a Cl^- ion? [1 mark]

The Periodic Table

We haven't always known as much about chemistry as we do now. No sirree. Take the periodic table. Early chemists looked to try and understand patterns in the elements' properties to get a bit of understanding.

Dmitri Mendeleev Made the First Proper Periodic Table

1) In 1869, Dmitri Mendeleev took the 50 or so elements known at the time and arranged them into his Table of Elements — with various gaps as shown.

2) Mendeleev put the elements in order of atomic mass. To keep elements with similar properties in the same vertical groups, he had to swap one or two elements round and leave a few gaps. He was prepared to leave some very big gaps in the first two rows before the transition metals come in on the third row.

Mendeleev's Table of the Elements

```
H
Li  Be                                              B  C  N  O  F
Na  Mg                                              Al Si P  S  Cl
K   Ca  *   Ti V  Cr Mn Fe Co Ni Cu Zn  *  *  As Se Br
Rb  Sr  Y   Zr Nb Mo *  Ru Rh Pd Ag Cd In Sn Sb Te I
Cs  Ba  *   *  Ta W  *  Os Ir Pt Au Hg Tl Pb Bi
```

3) The gaps were the really clever bit because they predicted the properties of so far undiscovered elements. When they were found and they fitted the pattern, it helped confirm Mendeleev's ideas. For example, Mendeleev made really good predictions about the chemical and physical properties of an element he called ekasilicon, which we know today as germanium.

This is How the Periodic Table Looks Today

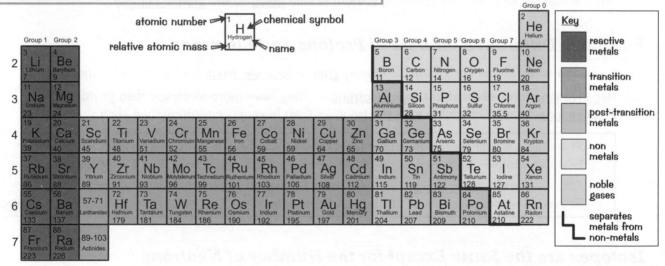

1) Once protons and electrons were discovered, the atomic number (see p.15) of each element could be found, based on the number of protons in its nucleus. The modern periodic table shows the elements in order of ascending atomic number — and they fit the same patterns that Mendeleev worked out.

2) The periodic table is laid out so elements with similar chemical properties form columns — these are called groups. (Elements with similar chemical properties react in similar ways.)

3) The group to which the element belongs corresponds to the number of electrons it has in its outer shell. E.g. Group 1 elements have 1 outer shell electron, Group 7 elements have 7, etc. Group 0 elements are the exception — they have full outer shells of 8 electrons (or 2 in the case of helium).

4) The rows are called periods. Each new period represents another full shell of electrons (see next page).

5) The period to which the element belongs corresponds to the number of shells of electrons it has.

I'm in a chemistry band — I play the symbols...

Because of how the periodic table is organised in groups and periods, you can see the trends in the reactivity (and other properties) of the elements and therefore make predictions on how reactions will occur. How neat is that?

Q1   Using a periodic table, state how many electrons beryllium has in its outer shell.   [1 mark]

Q2   Based on its position in the periodic table, would you expect the chemical properties of potassium to be more similar to those of sodium or calcium? Explain your answer.   [2 marks]

Electron Shells

Like snails, electrons live in shells. Unlike snails, electrons won't nibble on your petunias...

Electron Shell Rules:

1) Electrons occupy shells (sometimes called energy levels).
2) The lowest energy levels are always filled first.
3) Only a certain number of electrons are allowed in each shell:

1st shell	2nd shell	3rd shell
2 electrons	8 electrons	8 electrons

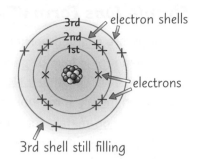

3rd shell still filling

Working Out Electronic Structures

The electronic structures for the first 20 elements are shown in the diagram below.
They're not hard to work out. For a quick example, take nitrogen:

1) The periodic table tells you that nitrogen has seven protons, so it must have seven electrons.
2) Follow the 'Electron Shell Rules' above. The first shell can only take 2 electrons and the second shell can take a maximum of 8 electrons.
3) So the electronic structure for nitrogen must be 2.5 — easy peasy.

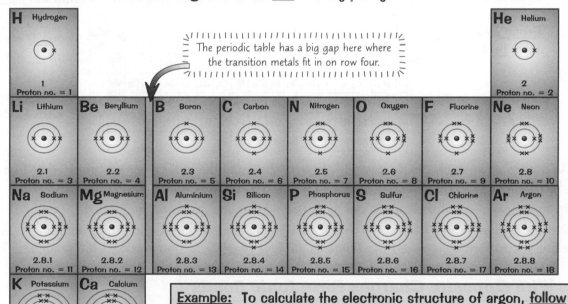

The periodic table has a big gap here where the transition metals fit in on row four.

Example: To calculate the electronic structure of argon, follow the rules. It's got 18 protons, so it must have 18 electrons. The first shell must have 2 electrons, the second shell must have 8, and so the third shell must have 8 as well. It's as easy as 2.8.8.

You can also work out the electronic structure of an element from its period and group.

- The number of shells which contain electrons is the same as the period of the element.
- The group number tells you how many electrons occupy the outer shell of the element.

Example: Sodium is in period 3, so it has 3 shells occupied — so the first two shells must be full (2.8). It's in Group 1, so it has 1 electron in its outer shell. So its electronic structure is 2.8.1.

The electronic structure of the fifth element — it's a bit boron...

Electronic structures may seem a bit complicated at first but once you learn the rules, it's a piece of cake.

Q1 Give the electronic structure of aluminium (atomic number = 13). 2, 8, 3 [1 mark]

Q2 In which group and period of the periodic table would you expect to find the element with electronic structure 2.8.8.2? [2 marks]

Topic C2 — Elements, Compounds and Mixtures

Ionic Bonding

Ions crop up all over the place in chemistry — some atoms just can't wait to get rid of <u>electrons</u>, others wish they had just one or two more. It's like... something, I don't know... just make up your own metaphor...

Simple Ions Form When Atoms Lose or Gain Electrons

1) <u>Ions</u> are <u>charged</u> particles — they can be <u>single atoms</u> (e.g. Cl^-) or <u>groups of atoms</u> (e.g. NO_3^-).

2) When <u>atoms</u> lose or gain electrons to form ions, all they're trying to do is get a <u>full outer shell</u> (also called a "<u>stable electronic structure</u>"). Atoms like full outer shells — it's atom heaven.

3) When <u>metals</u> form ions, they <u>lose</u> electrons to form <u>positive ions</u>.

4) When <u>non-metals</u> form ions, they <u>gain</u> electrons to form <u>negative ions</u>.

5) The <u>number</u> of electrons lost or gained is the same as the <u>charge</u> on the ion.
E.g. If 2 electrons are <u>lost</u> the charge is 2+. If 3 electrons are <u>gained</u> the charge is 3–.

Groups 1 & 2 and 6 & 7 are the Most Likely to Form Ions

1) The elements that most readily form ions are those in <u>Groups 1</u>, <u>2</u>, <u>6</u> and <u>7</u>.

2) <u>Group 1 and 2 elements</u> are <u>metals</u>. They <u>lose</u> electrons to form <u>positive ions</u> (<u>cations</u>).

3) <u>Group 6 and 7 elements</u> are <u>non-metals</u>. They <u>gain</u> electrons to form <u>negative ions</u> (<u>anions</u>).

4) Elements in the same <u>group</u> all have the same number of <u>outer electrons</u>. So they have to <u>lose or gain</u> the same number to get a full outer shell. And this means that they form ions with the <u>same charges</u>.

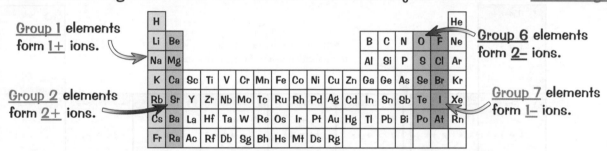

<u>Group 1</u> elements form <u>1+</u> ions.

<u>Group 2</u> elements form <u>2+</u> ions.

<u>Group 6</u> elements form <u>2–</u> ions.

<u>Group 7</u> elements form <u>1–</u> ions.

5) As you go <u>down</u> each group, you <u>add electron shells</u>, so the <u>outer electrons</u> get <u>further</u> from the nucleus.

6) For <u>Groups 1 and 2</u>, this means that it gets <u>easier</u> to <u>remove</u> the outer electrons to form <u>ions</u> — so the elements get <u>more reactive</u> as you go down the groups.

7) But for <u>Groups 6 and 7</u>, it means that it gets <u>harder</u> for the nucleus to <u>attract</u> extra electrons to form <u>ions</u> — so the elements get <u>less reactive</u> as you go down the groups.

Ions With Opposite Charges Form Ionic Bonds

When a <u>metal</u> and a <u>non-metal</u> react together, the <u>metal</u> can <u>lose</u> electrons to form a <u>positively charged ion</u> and the <u>non-metal</u> can <u>gain electrons</u> to form a <u>negatively charged ion</u>. These oppositely charged ions are then <u>strongly attracted</u> to one another by <u>electrostatic forces</u> and form an <u>ionic bond</u>.

To find the <u>formula</u> of an ionic compound, you <u>balance</u> the positive and the negative charges. For example:

Sodium chloride	Magnesium chloride	Potassium oxide
$Na^+ + Cl^- \longrightarrow NaCl$	$Mg^{2+} + 2Cl^- \longrightarrow MgCl_2$	$2K^+ + O^{2-} \longrightarrow K_2O$
The <u>sodium</u> ion has a 1+ charge and the <u>chloride</u> ion has a 1– charge, so they balance.	The <u>magnesium</u> ion has a 2+ charge and the <u>chloride</u> ion has a 1– charge, so you need <u>two</u> Cl^- ions to balance the Mg^{2+} ion.	The <u>potassium</u> ion has a 1+ charge and the <u>oxygen</u> ion has a 2– charge, so you need <u>two</u> K^+ ions to balance the O^{2-} ion.

Any old ion, any old ion — any, any, any old ion...

Make sure you know why ions form, how to work out what ions different elements form, and how ionic bonds form.

Q1 Describe, in terms of electron transfer, how potassium (K) and chlorine (Cl) react to form potassium chloride (KCl).

[3 marks]

Ionic Compounds

Here's a bit more about how ionic compounds form and the properties that make them special...

You Can Show Ionic Bonding Using Dot and Cross Diagrams

Dot and cross diagrams show the <u>arrangement</u> of electrons in an atom or ion. They can also show what happens to the electrons when atoms <u>react</u> with each other. Each electron is represented by a <u>dot</u> or a <u>cross</u>.

<u>Sodium Chloride (NaCl)</u>
The <u>sodium</u> atom gives up its outer electron, becoming an <u>Na$^+$</u> ion. The <u>chlorine</u> atom picks up the electron, becoming a <u>Cl$^-$</u> (<u>chloride</u>) ion.

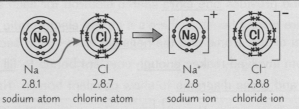

Na
2.8.1
sodium atom

Cl
2.8.7
chlorine atom

Na$^+$
2.8
sodium ion

Cl$^-$
2.8.8
chloride ion

Here, the dots represent the Na electrons and the crosses represent the Cl electrons (all electrons are really identical, but this is a good way of following their movement).

<u>Magnesium Chloride (MgCl$_2$)</u>
The <u>magnesium</u> atom gives up its <u>two</u> outer electrons, becoming an <u>Mg^{2+}</u> ion. The two <u>chlorine</u> atoms pick up <u>one electron each</u>, becoming <u>two Cl$^-$</u> (chloride) ions.

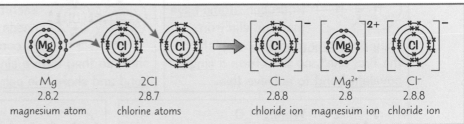

Mg
2.8.2
magnesium atom

2Cl
2.8.7
chlorine atoms

Cl$^-$
2.8.8
chloride ion

Mg^{2+}
2.8
magnesium ion

Cl$^-$
2.8.8
chloride ion

Dot and cross diagrams are really useful for showing how ionic compounds are formed, but they <u>don't</u> show the <u>structure</u> of the compound. For that, you'll need a different type of diagram.

Ionic Compounds Have a Regular Lattice Structure

<u>Ionic compounds</u> always have <u>giant ionic lattice</u> structures. The ions form a closely packed <u>regular lattice</u>. There are very strong <u>electrostatic forces of attraction</u> between <u>oppositely charged</u> ions, in <u>all directions</u>.

A single crystal of <u>sodium chloride</u> (salt) is <u>one giant ionic lattice</u>. The <u>Na$^+$</u> and <u>Cl$^-$</u> ions are held together in a regular lattice.

This model shows the scale of the ions, but it only lets you see the outer layer of the compound.

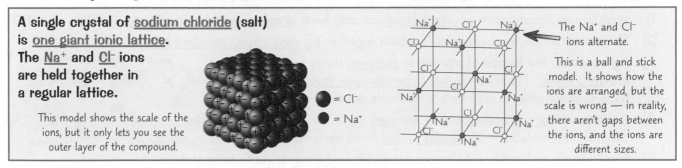

$= Cl^-$
$= Na^+$

The Na$^+$ and Cl$^-$ ions alternate.

This is a ball and stick model. It shows how the ions are arranged, but the scale is wrong — in reality, there aren't gaps between the ions, and the ions are different sizes.

Ionic Compounds All Have Similar Properties

1) Ionic compounds have <u>high melting</u> and <u>boiling points</u> due to the <u>strong attraction</u> between the ions. It takes a large amount of <u>energy</u> to overcome this attraction.

2) Solid ionic compounds <u>don't</u> conduct electricity because the ions are fixed in place and can't move. But when an ionic compound <u>melts</u>, the ions are <u>free to move</u> and will <u>carry an electric current</u>.

3) Many also <u>dissolve easily</u> in water. The ions <u>separate</u> and are all <u>free to move</u> in the solution, so they'll <u>carry an electric current</u>.

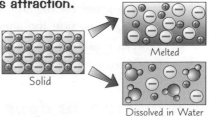

Melted

Solid

Dissolved in Water

Giant ionic lattices — all over your chips...

Make sure you know the advantages and disadvantages of each of the ways of drawing an ionic compound.

Q1   Draw a dot and cross diagram to show how potassium (electronic structure 2.8.8.1) and chlorine (electronic structure 2.8.7) react to form potassium chloride (KCl).   [3 marks]

Q2   Explain why the ionic compound caesium chloride conducts electricity when it is molten.   [1 mark]

Simple Molecules

Ionic bonding isn't the only way atoms join together. They can also <u>share</u> electrons to form <u>covalent bonds</u>.

Covalent Bonds — Sharing Electrons

1) When <u>non-metal atoms</u> combine together, they form <u>covalent bonds</u> by <u>sharing</u> pairs of electrons.

2) This way, <u>both atoms</u> feel that they have <u>a full outer shell</u>, and that makes them happy.

3) <u>Each</u> covalent bond provides <u>one extra</u> shared electron for each atom.

4) Covalent bonds are strong because there's a strong <u>electrostatic attraction</u> between the <u>positive</u> nuclei of the atoms and the <u>negative</u> electrons in each shared pair.

5) Usually, each atom involved makes <u>enough</u> covalent bonds to <u>fill up</u> its outer shell.

6) You can use <u>dot and cross diagrams</u> to show covalent bonds. Here are a few examples:

 <u>Hydrogen Gas: H_2</u>
Hydrogen atoms have just one electron.
They need <u>one more</u> to complete the first shell, so they form a <u>single covalent bond</u> to achieve this.

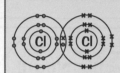 <u>Chlorine Gas: Cl_2</u>
Each chlorine atom needs <u>one electron</u> to complete its outer shell, so they form <u>a single covalent bond</u> and share <u>one pair</u> of electrons.

As in the dot and cross diagrams for ionic bonds on page 19, the dots and crosses here represent electrons from different atoms — but in reality all the electrons are identical.

 <u>Water: H_2O</u>
Oxygen needs <u>two</u> more electrons to fill its outer shell. In a molecule of water, it <u>shares</u> electrons with two hydrogen atoms, forming two single covalent bonds.

 <u>Carbon Dioxide: CO_2</u>
Carbon needs <u>four</u> more electrons to fill its outer shell, oxygen needs <u>two</u>. So <u>two double covalent bonds</u> are formed. A double covalent bond has <u>two shared pairs</u> of electrons.

Simple Molecular Substances Have Low Melting and Boiling Points

1) Substances formed with <u>covalent bonds</u> usually have <u>simple molecular structures</u>, like CO_2 and H_2O.

2) The atoms within the molecules are held together by <u>very strong covalent bonds</u>.

3) By contrast, the forces of attraction <u>between</u> these molecules are <u>very weak</u>. It's these <u>feeble intermolecular forces</u> that you have to overcome to melt or boil a simple covalent compound.

4) So the melting and boiling points are <u>very low</u>, because the molecules are <u>easily parted</u> from each other.

5) Most simple molecular substances are <u>gases or liquids</u> at room temperature.

6) Simple molecular substances <u>don't conduct electricity</u>, because they <u>don't</u> have free electrons or ions.

weak intermolecular forces

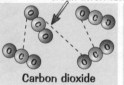 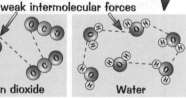

Carbon dioxide   Water

<u>Ball and stick models</u> show how the atoms in covalent molecules are connected. You can make them with plastic molecular model kits, or as computer models.

Ball and stick model of ethanol (C_2H_5OH)

- They're great for helping to <u>visualise</u> the structure of molecules, as they show you the shape of the molecule in <u>3D</u>.

- They're <u>more realistic</u> than 2D drawings, but they're still a bit <u>misleading</u>. They make it look like there are <u>massive gaps</u> between the atoms — in reality this is where the <u>electron clouds</u> interact.

Is it just me, or does ethanol look like a little doggie...

Covalent bonding is all about what's in an atom's outer electron shell. Make sure you're up to speed with electronic structures (see page 17) so you can work out how many covalent bonds an atom can form.

Q1   Given that fluorine atoms have the electronic structure 2.7, draw a dot and cross diagram to show the covalent bonding in a fluorine molecule, F_2.   [1 mark]

Q2   In a methane molecule, CH_4, a carbon atom is covalently bonded to four hydrogen atoms. Draw a dot and cross diagram to show the bonding in a methane molecule.   [1 mark]

Giant Covalent Structures and Fullerenes

Most of the <u>covalent molecules</u> you'll meet at GCSE contain only a few atoms. But not these beauties...

Giant Covalent Structures Contain Many Covalent Bonds

1) <u>Giant covalent structures</u> are similar to giant ionic lattices <u>except</u> that there are <u>no charged ions</u>.
2) The atoms are <u>bonded</u> to <u>each other</u> by <u>strong</u> covalent bonds.
3) This means that they have <u>very high</u> melting and boiling points.
4) They <u>don't conduct electricity</u> — not even when <u>molten</u> (except for graphite, graphene and fullerenes — see below).

Giant covalent structures are sometimes called 'macromolecules'. 'Macro-' means 'big'. They're called that because they're molecules, and they're big. Big for molecules, anyway.

5) The examples of <u>giant covalent structures</u> you need to know about are made from <u>carbon atoms</u>.
6) <u>Carbon</u> can form <u>loads</u> of different types of molecule (including the examples below), because carbon atoms can form up to <u>four covalent bonds</u>, and bond easily to <u>other carbon atoms</u> to make <u>chains</u> and <u>rings</u>. Some important <u>families</u> of <u>organic</u> (carbon-containing) compounds are covered on p.88-89.

Diamond

1) Pure diamonds are <u>lustrous</u> (sparkly) and <u>colourless</u>. Ideal for jewellery.
2) Each carbon atom forms <u>four covalent bonds</u> in a <u>very rigid</u> giant covalent structure, which makes diamond <u>really hard</u>. This makes diamonds ideal as cutting tools.
3) All those <u>strong covalent bonds</u> take a lot of energy to break and give diamond a <u>very high melting point</u>, which is another reason diamond is a good <u>cutting tool</u>.
4) It <u>doesn't conduct electricity</u> because it has <u>no free electrons</u> or ions.

Graphite and Graphene

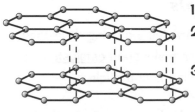

1) Graphite is <u>black</u> and <u>opaque</u>, but still kind of <u>shiny</u>.
2) Each carbon atom only forms <u>three covalent bonds</u>, creating <u>sheets of carbon atoms</u> which are free to <u>slide over each other</u>.
3) The layers are held together weakly so they are slippery and can be <u>rubbed off</u> onto paper to leave a black mark — that's how a pencil works. This also makes graphite ideal as a <u>lubricating material</u>.
4) Graphite's got a <u>high melting point</u> — the covalent bonds need <u>loads of energy</u> to break.
5) Since only three out of each carbon's four outer electrons are used in bonds, there are lots of <u>delocalised</u> (free) <u>electrons</u> that can move. This means graphite <u>conducts electricity</u>.

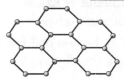

6) A single sheet of graphite is called <u>graphene</u>. Graphene's a bit of a wonder material — its covalent bonds make it extremely <u>strong</u> and a sheet of graphene is so thin that it's <u>transparent</u> and incredibly <u>light</u>. Its delocalised electrons are <u>completely free</u> to move about, which makes it even better at <u>conducting electricity</u> than graphite.

Fullerenes are Large Carbon Molecules

1) <u>Fullerenes</u> are another form of <u>carbon</u>. They aren't giant covalent structures, they're large <u>molecules</u> shaped like <u>hollow balls</u> or <u>tubes</u>. Different fullerenes contain <u>different numbers</u> of carbon atoms.
2) The carbon atoms in fullerenes are arranged in <u>rings</u>, similar to those in graphite. And like graphite, they have <u>delocalised electrons</u> so they can <u>conduct electricity</u>.

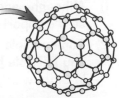

3) Their <u>melting</u> and <u>boiling points</u> aren't anything like as high as those of diamond and graphite, but they're <u>pretty high</u> for <u>molecular substances</u> because they're big molecules (and bigger molecules have more <u>intermolecular forces</u>).

So that pencil I gave her was just the same as a diamond, really...

Fullerenes are an example of nanoparticles — there's loads more about nanoparticles on the next page.

Q1 Give two similarities and two differences between diamond and graphite, in terms of their structure and properties. [4 marks]

Nanoparticles

Time for some properly cutting-edge science now. <u>Nanoparticles</u> have loads of really <u>useful properties</u> and new uses for them are being developed all the time.

Nanoparticles Are Really Really Really Really Tiny

1) Really tiny particles, <u>1–100 nanometers</u> across, are called 'nanoparticles' (1 nm = 0.000 000 001 m). Nanoparticles contain roughly <u>a few hundred atoms</u> — so they're <u>bigger</u> than <u>atoms</u> and <u>simple molecules</u>, but smaller than pretty much anything else.

2) <u>Fullerenes</u> (see previous page) are nanoparticles. The fullerenes include <u>nanotubes</u> — tiny hollow carbon tubes. All those covalent bonds make carbon nanotubes <u>very strong</u>.

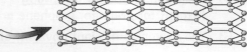

3) A nanoparticle has very <u>different properties</u> from the 'bulk' chemical that it's made from — e.g. <u>fullerenes</u> have different properties from big <u>lumps of carbon</u>.

Nanoparticles Have a High Surface Area to Volume Ratio

> **surface area to volume ratio = surface area ÷ volume**

1) As particles <u>decrease</u> in size, the size of their surface area <u>increases</u> in relation to their volume — so their surface area to volume ratio <u>increases</u>.

2) Nanoparticles have a really <u>high</u> surface area to volume ratio.

3) This gives them <u>different properties</u> from larger particles, because a much <u>greater proportion</u> of their atoms are available to interact with substances they come into contact with.

Nanoparticles Can Modify the Properties of Materials

Using nanoparticles is known as <u>nanoscience</u>. Many <u>new uses</u> of nanoparticles are being developed:

• They have a <u>huge surface area to volume ratio</u> (see above), so they can make good <u>catalysts</u> (see p.72).

• New cosmetics, e.g. <u>sun creams</u> and <u>deodorants</u>, have been made using nanoparticles. The small particles do their job but don't leave <u>white marks</u> on the skin.

• <u>Nanomedicine</u> is a hot topic. The idea is that tiny fullerenes are <u>absorbed</u> more easily by the body than most particles. This means they could <u>deliver drugs</u> right into the cells where they're needed.

• New <u>lubricant coatings</u> are being developed using fullerenes. These coatings reduce friction a bit like really tiny <u>ball bearings</u> and could be used in all sorts of places from <u>artificial joints</u> to <u>gears</u>.

• Nanotubes <u>conduct</u> electricity, so they can be used in tiny <u>electric circuits</u> for computer chips.

• Nanoparticles are added to <u>plastics</u> in <u>sports equipment</u>, e.g. tennis rackets, golf clubs and golf balls. They make the plastic much <u>stronger</u> and <u>more durable</u>, without adding much <u>mass</u> (hardly any in fact).

• <u>Silver nanoparticles</u> are added to the <u>polymer fibres</u> used to make <u>surgical masks</u> and <u>wound dressings</u>. This gives the fibres <u>antibacterial properties</u>.

The Effects of Nanoparticles on Health Aren't Fully Understood

1) Although nanoparticles are useful, the way they affect <u>the body</u> isn't fully understood, so it's important that any new nanoparticle products are <u>tested</u> thoroughly to minimise the risks.

2) Some people are worried that <u>products</u> containing nanoparticles have been made available <u>before</u> any possible <u>harmful</u> effects on <u>human health</u> have been investigated <u>properly</u> — in other words, we don't know what the <u>side effects</u> or <u>long-term</u> impacts on health could be.

Not to be confused with my Irish granny, Nan O'Flaherty...

It seems like small particles are big business — but as with any new tech, there are pros and cons. Make sure you've got a handle on why nanoparticles act differently from big particles.

Q1   Give three examples of uses of nanoparticles.   [3 marks]

Polymers and Properties of Materials

<u>Polymers</u> are yet another type of structure that you'll come across. They're a type of <u>covalent</u> molecule — but they behave differently to simple covalent substances because of the <u>long</u>, <u>thin shapes</u> of their molecules.

Plastics are Long-Chain Molecules Called Polymers

1) <u>Polymers</u> are formed when lots of small molecules called <u>monomers</u> join together.
This reaction is called <u>polymerisation</u> — and it usually needs high pressure and a catalyst.

2) Plastics are polymers. They're usually <u>carbon based</u> and their monomers are often <u>alkenes</u> — see p.88.

Forces Between Molecules Determine the Properties of Polymers

<u>Strong covalent</u> bonds hold the <u>atoms</u> together in <u>polymer chains</u>.
But it's the forces <u>between</u> the different chains that determine the <u>properties</u> of the plastic.

Squawk!
Pretty polymers!

Weak Forces:

If the plastic is made up of chains that are only held together by <u>weak intermolecular forces</u>, then the chains will be free to <u>slide</u> over each other. This means that the plastic can be <u>stretched easily</u>, and will have a <u>low melting point</u>.

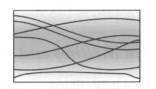

Strong Forces:

Some plastics have <u>stronger</u> bonds <u>between</u> the polymer chains — these might be <u>covalent bonds</u> (sometimes called <u>cross-links</u>). These plastics have <u>higher melting points</u>, are <u>rigid</u> and <u>can't be stretched</u>, as the <u>cross-links</u> hold the chains firmly together.

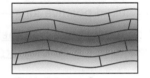

Properties of Materials Depend on Structure and Bonding

1) All the different <u>types of material</u> in this topic have their own special <u>properties</u>. What they've all got in common is the fact that their properties are down to the <u>structures</u> and <u>bonding</u> in the material.

2) The <u>individual atoms</u> in the material <u>don't</u> have these properties themselves — it's the type and strength of the bonds in a material that determines its properties.

> Properties of a whole material, rather than the individual atoms are called the bulk properties.

For example, <u>chlorine</u> is pretty good at forming both ionic and covalent bonds.

- It's found in many common <u>ionic compounds</u> like sodium chloride.
The <u>ionic bonds</u> in sodium chloride are <u>really strong</u>, because there's strong <u>electrostatic attraction</u> between the ions, which acts in all directions within the <u>lattice structure</u>. The strength of these bonds is what gives sodium chloride its <u>high melting and boiling point</u>.

- Chlorine also forms <u>simple molecular</u> substances such as chloromethane. Although the <u>covalent bonds</u> which hold together the atoms in each molecule of chloromethane are <u>very strong</u>, the <u>intermolecular forces</u> which attract the molecules to each other are <u>weak</u> and easily overcome. So chloromethane has a <u>low melting and boiling point</u>.

- Some <u>polymers</u>, such as polyvinyl chloride (PVC), also contain chlorine. PVC is <u>strong</u> and <u>rigid</u>, because the <u>intermolecular forces</u> between the <u>polymer chains</u> in PVC are relatively <u>strong</u>.

Sodium chloride, chloromethane and PVC have these different properties because of the <u>structure</u> and <u>bonding</u> of each substance, <u>not</u> because they contain chlorine atoms. Chlorine just happens to be able to form the bonds you need to make these structures.

My cat Molly loves plastics — in fact, Molly purrs for polymers...

Polymers are really useful. If the stuff about them on this page has whetted your appetite for all things polymer-y, you'll be pleased to know that there's more about them on pages 90-91. Bet you can't wait.

Q1 Two polymers, A and B, are both composed entirely of carbon and hydrogen. Polymer A has a high melting point and is very rigid. Polymer B has a low melting point and is fairly flexible. Suggest why these polymers have different properties, despite being composed of the same elements. [3 marks]

Metals

BONG. Here is the news. BONG. Metals have some really useful properties. BONG. These properties come from the bonding in metals. BONG. Okay, I'll stop hitting myself with this metal pan now.

Metals Have a Crystal Structure

1) All metals have the same basic properties, due to the special type of bonding that exists in metals.

2) In metals, the outer electron(s) of each atom can move freely. The atoms become positive ions in a 'sea' of delocalised (free) electrons.

3) Metallic bonding is the electrostatic attraction between these ions and electrons. The ions are surrounded by the electrons, so the attraction acts in all directions.

4) This bonding is what gives rise to many of the properties of metals.

Metals generally hang out on the left-hand side of the periodic table. This explains the bonding in solid metals — elements on the left of the table normally get a full outer shell by losing electrons (see p.18), so metal atoms find it easy to become positive ions. The electrons they give up form the electron 'sea'.

Most Have High Melting and Boiling Points, and High Density

1) Metals are very hard, dense and lustrous (i.e. shiny).

2) There's a strong attraction between the delocalised electrons and the closely packed positive ions — causing very strong metallic bonding.

3) Metals generally have high melting and boiling points because of these strong metallic bonds. You need to use a lot of energy to break them apart.

They're Strong, but Also Bendy and Malleable

1) Metals have a high tensile strength — they're strong and hard to break.

2) But they can also be hammered into different shapes (they're malleable).

They're Good Conductors of Heat and Electricity

1) This is entirely due to the sea of delocalised electrons which move freely through the metal, carrying the electrical current.

2) They can also carry heat energy through the metal.

Don't try this at home. You'll die.

They React with Oxygen to Form Metal Oxides

Most metals can react with oxygen to form metal oxides. Most metal oxides are solid at room temperature and form basic solutions when you dissolve them in water (see p.43 for more on bases).

Non-metals also react with oxygen to form oxides. Non-metal oxides tend to form acidic solutions in water.

They Can be Mixed with Other Elements to Make Alloys

1) Pure metals often aren't quite right for certain jobs. You can change metals properties by mixing them with other elements (either metals or non-metals) to make alloys.

2) Alloys have different properties from the main metal (or metals) they contain. For example, they may be stronger, more malleable or more corrosion resistant.

There's more about alloys on page 78.

Non-metal elements generally have different properties from metals. Non-metals usually have low melting and boiling points and, when solid, they tend to be weak and brittle. They have lower densities than metals and don't conduct electricity. (But there are exceptions, e.g. carbon breaks some of these rules — see p.21.)

I saw a metal on the bus once — he was the conductor...

If your knowledge of metals is still feeling a bit delocalised, the question below will help...

Q1 Copper is a metallic element. State what property of copper makes it suitable for using in electrical circuits, and explain why it has this property. [2 marks]

States, Structure and Bonding

Bridge vs lighthouse... Phone box vs pyramid... It's time to start comparing different types of structure...

Structure and Bonding Affect Melting and Boiling Points

1) The type of bonding in a substance affects its melting point and boiling point.
It's all to do with how much energy you need to put in to get the atoms, ions or molecules apart.

2) The stronger the bonds are that keep the particles together in a solid or liquid, the more heat energy you need to put in to overcome those bonds and separate the particles.

3) Simple covalent substances have strong bonds within each molecule, but only weak intermolecular forces between the molecules (see p.20). It doesn't take much energy to overcome these forces, so simple covalent substances melt and boil at fairly low temperatures.

Structure	Melting / boiling point
simple covalent	low
metallic	high
ionic	high
giant covalent	high

4) Most metals have high melting and boiling points because the metal ions are very strongly attracted to the delocalised electron 'sea' (see p.24).

5) The positive and negative ions in ionic lattices are strongly attracted to each other. This strong electrostatic attraction means ionic substances have high melting and boiling points.

6) Giant covalent lattices are held together by strong covalent bonds. These bonds take a lot of energy to break, so giant covalent substances have very high melting and boiling points. (In fact, some giant covalent substances sublime instead — that means they go straight from a solid to a gas.)

Making Predictions about Substances from their Properties

You might be asked to use data about substances to work out what type of substance they are or how they behave in certain conditions.

EXAMPLE: The table below give information about the properties of four different substances.

Substance	Melting point / °C	Boiling point / °C	Good electrical conductor?
A	−218.4	−183.0	No
B	1535	2750	Yes
C	1410	2355	No
D	801	1413	When molten

How well different types of substance conduct electricity is covered on p.19-21 and p.24.

a) Predict the structure of substance C.
1) C has a high melting and boiling point, so it's unlikely to be a simple molecular substance.
2) It doesn't conduct electricity well, so that means it's unlikely to be a metal. Ionic substances don't conduct electricity when they're solid, but they do when they're liquid, so we can rule out ionic too.
3) Giant covalent structures don't usually conduct electricity, and they have high melting and boiling points, so this is probably the structure of C.

Substance C is likely to have a giant covalent structure.

b) Predict the state of substance D at 1000 °C.
1) The melting point of D is 801 °C and its boiling point is 1413 °C.
2) That means it's a solid below 801 °C, a gas above 1413 °C, and a liquid in between.
3) 1000 °C is between 801 °C and 1413 °C, so D is a liquid at this temperature.

Substance D will be a liquid at 1000 °C.

I predict a tall, dark examiner will set you a question on this...

Questions on this sort of stuff may well require you to put all the bits of info from the last few pages together. Remember, you need to know what properties the different types of structure have and why they have them too.

Q1 Using the table in the example above:
a) Predict the states of substances A, B and C at 1500 °C. [3 marks]
b) Predict the structures of substances A, B and D. Explain your answers. [6 marks]

Purity

<u>Purity</u> — one of those special <u>science words</u> that has a special <u>science meaning</u> that doesn't quite match the normal meaning people use in real life... *sigh*...

Pure Substances Contain Only One Thing

Having impure thoughts again, Henry?

1) In <u>everyday life</u>, the word '<u>pure</u>' is often used to mean 'clean' or 'natural'.

2) In <u>chemistry</u>, it's got a more <u>specific</u> meaning — a substance is <u>pure</u> if it's completely made up of a <u>single element or compound</u>.

3) If you've got <u>more than one</u> compound present, or different elements that aren't all part of a single compound, then you've got a <u>mixture</u>, not a pure substance.

4) So, for example, <u>fresh air</u> might be thought of as nice and 'pure', but it's <u>chemically impure</u>, because it's a mixture of nitrogen, oxygen, argon, carbon dioxide, water vapour and various other gases.

5) Lots of <u>mixtures</u> are really <u>useful</u> — <u>alloys</u> (see p.78) are a great example. But sometimes chemists need to obtain a <u>pure sample</u> of a substance.

Test For Purity Using Boiling and Melting Points

1) Every <u>pure</u> substance has a <u>specific melting point</u> and <u>boiling point</u>. For example, pure ice melts at 0 °C, and pure water boils at 100 °C.

2) So you can test the <u>purity</u> of a sample of a substance by comparing the <u>actual</u> melting or boiling point of the sample to the <u>expected value</u>.

3) If a substance is <u>impure</u>, the <u>melting point</u> will be too <u>low</u>. So if some ice melts at −2 °C, it's probably got an impurity in it (e.g. salt).

4) The <u>boiling point</u> of an impure substance will be too <u>high</u>. For example, seawater contains salt (and other impurities). Its boiling point tends to be around 100.6 °C.

5) You can also sometimes tell if a sample of a solid or liquid is a <u>mixture</u> by <u>heating it up</u>. In a mixture, the <u>different components</u> will melt or boil at <u>different temperatures</u>, so part of the mixture will melt or boil first, while the rest will stay in its original state for longer. This means mixtures will often melt over a <u>range</u> of temperatures.

> <u>Example:</u> Adil is testing a sample of a compound for <u>purity</u> by determining its <u>melting point</u>. The <u>pure compound</u> has a melting point of <u>55 °C</u>. Adil believes his sample contains a small number of <u>impurities</u>.
>
> If Adil is correct, which of the following results should he expect from his test?
>
> A. The sample melts at a temperature <u>below 55 °C</u>.
> B. The sample melts at <u>exactly 55 °C</u>.
> C. The sample melts at a temperature <u>above 55 °C</u>.
> D. The sample melts gradually over a <u>range of temperatures</u> which includes 55 °C.
>
> Answer: Impurities <u>lower</u> the melting point of a substance, so if his sample is impure, Adil should expect it to melt <u>below</u> the normal value.
>
> A. The sample melts at a temperature below 55 °C.

If in doubt, heat it up until it melts — that's my motto...

There are lots of ways to extract a pure substance out of a mixture. The ones you need to know about are covered over the next few pages. But first, let's check you've got your head around the concept of purity.

Q1   Rachel buys a carton of juice labelled '100% pure orange juice'. Explain why the use of the word 'pure' on this label doesn't match the scientific definition.   [2 marks]

Q2   Steel is produced by adding carbon to iron to make it stronger. Would you expect steel to have a higher or lower melting point then pure iron? Explain your answer.   [2 marks]

Distillation

Distillation is used to separate mixtures that contain <u>liquids</u>.
There are two types that you need to know about — <u>simple</u> and <u>fractional</u>.

Simple Distillation is Used to Separate Out Solutions

<u>Simple distillation</u> is used for separating out a <u>liquid</u> from a <u>solution</u>.
Here's how to use simple distillation to get <u>pure water</u> from <u>seawater</u>:

1) Pour your sample of seawater into the <u>distillation flask</u>.

2) Set up the <u>apparatus</u> as shown in the diagram. Connect the bottom end of the <u>condenser</u> to a cold tap using <u>rubber tubing</u>. Run <u>cold water</u> through the condenser to keep it cool.

3) Gradually heat the distillation flask. The part of the solution that has the lowest boiling point will <u>evaporate</u> — in this case, that's the water.

4) The water <u>vapour</u> passes into the condenser where it <u>cools</u> and <u>condenses</u> (turns back into a liquid). It then flows into the beaker where it is <u>collected</u>.

5) Eventually you'll end up with just the <u>salt</u> left in the flask.

The <u>problem</u> with simple distillation is that you can only use it to separate things with <u>very different</u> boiling points.

If you have a <u>mixture of liquids</u> with <u>similar boiling points</u>, you need another method to separate them out — like fractional distillation...

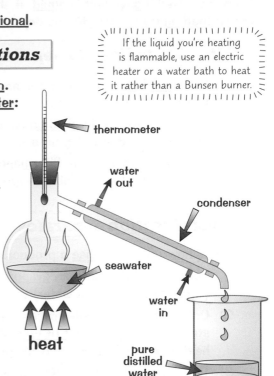

If the liquid you're heating is flammable, use an electric heater or a water bath to heat it rather than a Bunsen burner.

thermometer

water out

condenser

seawater

water in

heat

pure distilled water

Fractional Distillation is Used to Separate a Mixture of Liquids

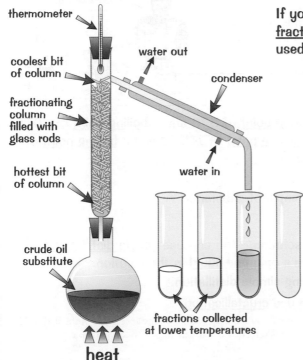

thermometer

coolest bit of column

fractionating column filled with glass rods

hottest bit of column

crude oil substitute

water out

condenser

water in

fractions collected at lower temperatures

heat

If you've got a <u>mixture of liquids</u> you can separate it using <u>fractional distillation</u>. Here's a lab demonstration that can be used to model <u>fractional distillation of crude oil</u> at a <u>refinery</u>:

1) Put your <u>mixture</u> in a flask. Attach a <u>fractionating column</u> and condenser above the flask as shown.

2) Gradually heat the flask. The <u>different liquids</u> will all have <u>different boiling points</u> — so they will evaporate at <u>different temperatures</u>.

3) The liquid with the <u>lowest boiling point</u> evaporates first. When the temperature on the thermometer matches the boiling point of this liquid, it will reach the <u>top</u> of the column.

4) Liquids with <u>higher boiling points</u> might also start to evaporate. But the column is <u>cooler</u> towards the <u>top</u>, so they will only get part of the way up before <u>condensing</u> and running back down towards the flask.

5) When the first liquid has been collected, <u>raise the temperature</u> until the <u>next one</u> reaches the top.

Fractionating — sounds a bit too much like maths to me...

The industrial method for fractional distillation of crude oil isn't quite as... well... crude as the one shown here. If you're desperate to find out what goes on in oil refineries, have a look at page 92.

Q1   Propan-1-ol, methanol and ethanol have boiling points of 97 °C, 65 °C and 78 °C respectively.
A student uses fractional distillation to separate a mixture of these compounds.
State which liquid will be collected in the second fraction and explain why.   [2 marks]

Filtration and Crystallisation

If you've mixed a <u>solid</u> with a <u>liquid</u>, it should be pretty easy to <u>separate</u> them out again. Which <u>method</u> you'll need to use depends on whether or not the solid can <u>dissolve</u> in the liquid.

Filtration is Used to Separate an Insoluble Solid from a Liquid

PRACTICAL

1) If the <u>product</u> of a reaction is an <u>insoluble solid</u>, you can use <u>filtration</u> to separate it out from the <u>liquid reaction mixture</u>.

2) It can be used in <u>purification</u> as well. For example, <u>solid impurities</u> can be separated out from a reaction mixture using <u>filtration</u>.

3) All you do is pop some <u>filter paper</u> into a <u>funnel</u> and pour your mixture into it. The liquid part of the mixture <u>runs through</u> the paper, leaving behind a <u>solid residue</u>.

Filter paper folded into a cone shape.

The solid is left in the filter paper.

Crystallisation Separates a Soluble Solid from a Solution

PRACTICAL

Here's how you <u>crystallise</u> a product...

1) Pour the solution into an <u>evaporating dish</u> and gently <u>heat</u> the solution. Some of the <u>solvent</u> (which will usually be water) will evaporate and the solution will get more <u>concentrated</u>.

2) Once some of the solvent has evaporated, <u>or</u> when you see crystals start to form (the <u>point of crystallisation</u>), remove the dish from the heat and leave the solution to <u>cool</u>.

evaporating dish

3) The salt should start to form <u>crystals</u> as it becomes <u>insoluble</u> in the cold, highly concentrated solution.

4) <u>Filter</u> the crystals out of the solution, and leave them in a warm place to <u>dry</u>. You could also use a <u>drying oven</u> or a <u>desiccator</u> (a desiccator contains chemicals that remove water from the surroundings).

Choose the Right Purification Method

You might have to pick one of the <u>techniques</u> covered in this section to separate a mixture. The best technique to use will depend on the <u>properties</u> of the <u>substances</u> in the mixture.

Choose wisely...

Example:
A <u>mixture</u> is composed of two substances, **X** and **Y**.
<u>Substance X</u> is a <u>liquid</u> at room temperature, has a <u>melting point</u> of 5 °C and a <u>boiling point</u> of 60 °C.
<u>Substance Y</u> is a <u>solid</u> at room temperature. It has a <u>melting point</u> of 745 °C and a <u>boiling point</u> of 1218 °C. Substance Y <u>dissolves completely</u> in substance X.

<u>Suggest</u> a <u>purification method</u> you could use to obtain:
a) A pure sample of substance X,   b) A pure sample of substance Y.

Answer:

a) To get X on its own, you need to <u>distil it</u> from the solution. You can use <u>simple distillation</u> here — there's no need for fractional distillation as there's only <u>one liquid</u> in the solution.
You could obtain a pure sample of substance X using simple distillation.

b) To get a <u>soluble solid</u> out of a solution, you should use <u>crystallisation</u>.
In theory, if you <u>distilled</u> the mixture until all of the liquid had evaporated off, you'd end up with just substance Y left in the flask. But there might be traces of substance X still hanging around too — crystallisation's a better way to be sure of getting a <u>pure sample</u> of a solid from a solution.
You could obtain a pure sample of substance Y using crystallisation.

Its mum calls it Philliptration...

Some mixtures are made up of several components, so you might need to use a combination of the methods covered in this section to get all the different components out.

Q1   You are given a solution that has been made by dissolving copper sulfate crystals in water. Describe a method you could use to extract pure copper sulfate crystals from the solution.   [4 marks]

Chromatography

Chromatography is one analytical method that you need to know inside out and upside down... read on.

Chromatography uses Two Phases

Chromatography is a method used to separate and identify the substances in a mixture.
There are lots of different types of chromatography — but they all have two 'phases':

- A mobile phase — where the molecules can move. This is always a liquid or a gas.
- A stationary phase — where the molecules can't move. This can be a solid or a really thick liquid.

1) The components in the mixture separate out as the mobile phase moves over the stationary phase — they all end up in different places in the stationary phase.

2) This happens because each of the chemicals in a mixture will spend different amounts of time dissolved in the mobile phase and stuck to the stationary phase (see below for more).

3) How fast a chemical moves through the stationary phase depends on how it 'distributes' itself between the two phases.

In Thin-Layer Chromatography the Mobile Phase is a Solvent | PRACTICAL

In thin-layer chromatography (TLC), the stationary phase is a thin layer of a solid (e.g. silica gel or aluminium oxide powder) on a glass or plastic plate. The mobile phase is a solvent (e.g. ethanol).

Here's the method for setting it up:

1) Draw a line near the bottom of the plate. (Use a pencil to do this — pencil marks are insoluble and won't move with the solvent as ink might.) Put a spot of the mixture to be separated on the line.

2) Put some of the solvent into a beaker. Dip the bottom of the plate (not the spot) into the solvent.

3) Put a watch glass over the beaker to stop any solvent from evaporating away.

4) The solvent will start to move up the plate. When the chemicals in the mixture dissolve in the solvent, they will move up the plate too.

5) You will see the different chemicals in the sample separate out, forming spots at different places on the plate.

6) Remove the plate from the beaker before the solvent reaches the top. Mark the distance the solvent has moved (the solvent front) in pencil.

watch glass
solvent front
plate
spot of unknown substance
point of origin
solvent

You could use this technique to separate the different components of a dye.

The amount of time the molecules spend in each phase depends on two things:

- How soluble they are in the solvent.
- How attracted they are to the stationary phase.

Molecules with a higher solubility in the solvent (and which are less attracted to the stationary phase) will spend more time in the mobile phase than the stationary phase — so they'll be carried further up the plate.

Paper Chromatography is Similar to TLC

1) Paper chromatography is very similar to TLC, but the stationary phase is a sheet of chromatography paper (often filter paper).

2) The mobile phase is a solvent such as ethanol (just like in TLC).

What's up with Barry?

He's going through a stationery phase.

Give that mixture a bit of TLC, baby...

You might get asked about TLC or paper chromatography in the exams — lucky they're so similar then...

Q1   A mixture of two chemicals, A and B, is separated using thin-layer chromatography.
Chemical A is more soluble in the solvent than B is. Which chemical, A or B,
will end up closer to the solvent front? Explain your answer.   [2 marks]

Topic C2 — Elements, Compounds and Mixtures

Interpreting Chromatograms

So, what use is <u>chromatography</u>, apart from making a pretty pattern of spots? Let's find out...

You can Calculate the R_f Value for Each Chemical

1) The result of chromatography analysis is called a <u>chromatogram</u>.

2) Sometimes, the spots on a chromatogram might be <u>colourless</u>. If they are, you'll need to use a <u>locating agent</u> to show where they are (e.g. you might have to <u>spray</u> the chromatogram with a special <u>reagent</u>).

3) You need to know how to work out the R_f <u>values</u> for <u>spots</u> (solutes) on a chromatogram.

4) An R_f value is the <u>ratio</u> between the distance travelled by the dissolved substance (the solute) and the distance travelled by the solvent. You can find R_f values using the formula:

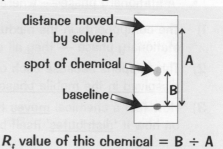

distance moved by solvent

spot of chemical

baseline

R_f value of this chemical = B ÷ A

$$R_f = \frac{\text{distance travelled by solute}}{\text{distance travelled by solvent}}$$

5) To find the distance travelled by the solute, measure from the <u>baseline</u> to the <u>centre of the spot</u>.

6) Chromatography is often carried out to see if a certain substance is present in a mixture. You run a <u>pure sample</u> of the substance alongside the unknown mixture. If the R_f values match, the substances may be the <u>same</u> (although it doesn't definitely prove they are the same).

7) Chemists sometimes run samples of pure substances called <u>standard reference materials</u> (SRMs) next to a mixture to check the identities of its components. SRMs have controlled <u>concentrations and purities</u>.

8) You can also use chromatography to do a <u>purity test</u>. A <u>pure</u> substance <u>won't</u> be <u>separated</u> by <u>chromatography</u> — it'll always move as <u>one blob</u>, while a <u>mixture</u> can produce <u>multiple blobs</u>.

Gas Chromatography is a Bit More High-Tech

<u>Gas chromatography</u> (GC) is used to analyse <u>unknown substances</u> too. If they're not already gases, then they have to be vaporised. The <u>mobile phase</u> is an <u>unreactive gas</u> such as nitrogen, and the <u>stationary phase</u> is a <u>viscous</u> (thick) <u>liquid</u>, such as an oil.

mobile phase enters here

sample injected

detector

tube coated with stationary phase

temperature controlled oven

The process is quite <u>different</u> from paper chromatography and TLC:

1) The unknown mixture is <u>injected</u> into a long tube <u>coated</u> on the inside with the <u>stationary phase</u>.

2) The mixture <u>moves</u> along the tube with the <u>mobile phase</u> until it <u>comes out</u> the other end. As in the other chromatography methods, the substances are <u>distributed</u> between the phases (so each substance spends <u>different amounts of time</u> dissolved in the mobile phase and stuck to the stationary phase).

3) The <u>time</u> it takes a chemical to <u>travel through</u> the tube is called the <u>retention time</u>.

4) The retention time is <u>different</u> for each chemical — that's what's used to <u>identify</u> it.

The <u>chromatogram</u> from GC is a graph. Each <u>peak</u> on the graph represents a <u>different chemical</u>.

- The <u>distance</u> along the x-axis is the <u>retention time</u> — which can be <u>looked up</u> to find out <u>what</u> the chemical is.

- The <u>relative areas</u> under the peaks show you the <u>relative amounts</u> of each chemical in the sample.

- There's one peak for each chemical, which means a sample of a <u>pure substance</u> will produce a <u>single peak</u>.

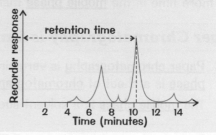

Recorder response

retention time

2 4 6 8 10 12 14
Time (minutes)

J'aime la chromatographie... hmm, I think I need an interpreter...

GC is used a lot by scientists in real-life chemical analysis. Just don't try it in your oven at home.

Q1 On a paper chromatogram, chemical X travelled 2.1 cm, chemical Y travelled 3.6 cm and the solvent front travelled 6.0 cm. Calculate the R_f value of chemical Y. [2 marks]

Relative Masses

The <u>mass of an atom</u> is really, really tiny. To make it easier to <u>calculate</u> with and <u>compare</u> the masses of different atoms, you usually use <u>relative masses</u> instead of their actual masses.

Relative Atomic Mass, A_r — Easy Peasy

In the periodic table, the elements all have <u>two</u> numbers next to them. The <u>bigger one</u> is the <u>relative atomic mass</u> (A_r) of the element.

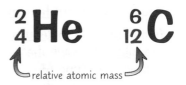

relative atomic mass

> The <u>relative atomic mass</u> of an element is the <u>average mass</u> of <u>one atom</u> of the element, compared to $\frac{1}{12}$ of the <u>mass</u> of <u>one atom</u> of <u>carbon-12</u>.

1) If an element only has <u>one isotope</u> (see p.15), its A_r will be the same as its <u>mass number</u>.

2) If an element has <u>more than one</u> isotope, its A_r will be the <u>average</u> of the <u>mass numbers</u> of <u>all the different isotopes</u>, taking into account <u>how much</u> there is of each one.

> <u>Example:</u> Chlorine has two stable isotopes, <u>chlorine-35</u> and <u>chlorine-37</u>. There's <u>quite a lot</u> of chlorine-35 around and <u>not so much</u> chlorine-37 — so chlorine's A_r works out as <u>35.5</u>.

Relative Formula Mass, M_r — Also Easy Peasy

The <u>relative formula mass</u>, $\underline{M_r}$, of a compound is all the relative atomic masses in its formula <u>added together</u>.

For simple covalent compounds, the relative formula mass is usually called the relative molecular mass.

EXAMPLE:

a) Find the relative formula mass of magnesium chloride, $MgCl_2$.

Use the <u>periodic table</u> to find the <u>relative atomic masses</u> of magnesium and chlorine.

$Mg + (2 \times Cl) = 24.3 + (2 \times 35.5)$
$= 24.3 + 71.0 = 95.3$

M_r of $MgCl_2 = 95.3$

b) Find the relative molecular mass of ethanoic acid, CH_3COOH.

Again, use the <u>periodic table</u> to find the <u>relative atomic masses</u> of carbon, hydrogen and oxygen. Then add them all up in the right proportions.

$C + (3 \times H) + C + O + O + H$
$= 12.0 + (3 \times 1.0) + 12.0 + 16.0 + 16.0 + 1.0$
$= 12.0 + 3.0 + 12.0 + 16.0 + 16.0 + 1.0 = 60.0$

M_r of $CH_3COOH = 60.0$

Compounds with Brackets in...

EXAMPLE:

Calcium hydroxide has the formula $Ca(OH)_2$.
Find the relative formula mass of calcium hydroxide.

The <u>small number 2</u> after the bracket in the formula $Ca(OH)_2$ means that <u>there's two of everything inside the brackets</u>.

$Ca + [(O + H) \times 2] = 40.1 + [(16.0 + 1.0) \times 2]$
$= 40.1 + 34.0 = 74.1$

M_r of $Ca(OH)_2 = 74.1$

This page is a relative masterpiece...

This stuff comes up a fair bit in chemistry, so make sure you've got to grips with it by doing loads of practice questions. Start with these. Use the periodic table on the back cover to find the A_r values you need.

Q1   Find the relative formula mass of sodium chloride, NaCl.   [1 mark]

Q2   Calculate the relative molecular mass of ethanol, C_2H_5OH.   [1 mark]

Q3   Find the relative formula mass of copper nitrate, $Cu(NO_3)_2$.   [2 marks]

Molecular and Empirical Formulas

Three types of <u>formula</u> to cover here. <u>Molecular</u> and <u>displayed</u> are pretty easy (and should already be familiar). <u>Empirical formulas</u> are a bit less fun, because they involve ratios, but I'm sure you'll learn to love them too...

Molecular Formulas and Displayed Formulas Show Numbers of Atoms

You can work out <u>how many atoms</u> of each type there are in a substance when you're given its <u>formula</u>.

This is called a <u>molecular formula</u>. It shows the <u>number</u> and <u>type</u> of <u>atoms</u> in a molecule.

CH_4

<u>Methane</u> contains 1 carbon atom and 4 hydrogen atoms.

H
|
H–C–H
|
H

This is called a <u>displayed formula</u>. It shows the <u>atoms</u> and the <u>covalent bonds</u> in a molecule as a picture.

Don't panic if a molecular formula has <u>brackets</u> in it — they're easy to deal with.

$CH_3(CH_2)_2CH_3$

For example, the 2 after the bracket here means that there are 2 lots of CH_2. So altogether there are 4 carbon atoms and 10 hydrogen atoms.

If you have the <u>displayed formula</u> of a molecule, you can use it to write the <u>molecular formula</u> (and vice versa) — each carbon atom in the molecular formula matches up with one carbon in the displayed formula.

```
   H H H H
   | | | |
H–C–C–C–C–H
   | | | |
   H H H H
```

$CH_3(CH_2)_2CH_3$

The Empirical Formula is the Simplest Ratio of Atoms

An <u>empirical formula</u> of a compound tells you the <u>smallest whole number ratio</u> of atoms in the compound.

EXAMPLE: Find the empirical formula of: a) Ethane, C_2H_6 b) Glucose, $C_6H_{12}O_6$

a) The numbers in the <u>molecular formula</u> of <u>ethane</u> are <u>2</u> and <u>6</u>. To simplify the ratio, divide by the largest number that goes into 2 and 6 <u>exactly</u> — that's <u>2</u>.

C: $2 \div 2 = 1$
H: $6 \div 2 = 3$

The empirical formula of ethane is CH_3.

b) The numbers in the <u>molecular formula</u> of <u>glucose</u> are <u>6</u>, <u>12</u> and <u>6</u>. To simplify the ratio, divide by the largest number that goes into 6, 12 and 6 <u>exactly</u> — that's <u>6</u>.

C: $6 \div 6 = 1$
H: $12 \div 6 = 2$
O: $6 \div 6 = 1$

The empirical formula of glucose is CH_2O.

You can use the <u>empirical formula</u> of a compound, together with its M_r, to find its molecular formula.

EXAMPLE: Compound X has the empirical formula C_2H_6N. The M_r of compound X is 88. Find the molecular formula of compound X.

1) Start by finding the M_r of the <u>empirical formula</u>. The A_r of carbon is <u>12</u>, the A_r of hydrogen is <u>1</u> and the A_r of nitrogen is <u>14</u>.

M_r of $C_2H_6N = (2 \times C) + (6 \times H) + N$
$= (2 \times 12.0) + (6 \times 1.0) + 14.0$
$= 24.0 + 6.0 + 14.0$
$= 44.0$

2) Divide the M_r of compound X by the M_r of the <u>empirical formula</u>.

$88 \div 44.0 = 2$

3) Now to get the <u>molecular formula</u> of compound X, you just <u>multiply</u> everything in the empirical formula by your answer to step 2) — in this case, that's <u>2</u>.

C: $2 \times 2 = 4$
H: $6 \times 2 = 12$
N: $1 \times 2 = 2$

The molecular formula of compound X is $C_4H_{12}N_2$.

I believe in empiricals...

Another page with lots of maths — which means the best way to learn this stuff is by doing some questions. Wait, what's that on the next line? A question on empirical formulas? It's almost like it's your destiny to answer it...

Q1   What is the empirical formula of a compound with the molecular formula $C_4H_8Cl_2$?   [1 mark]

Revision Questions for Topics C1 and C2

That's Topic C1 and Topic C2 done and dusted. Time to take a look back at the best bits.

- Try these questions and tick off each one when you get it right.
- When you've done all the questions under a heading and are completely happy with it, tick it off.

States of Matter and the Atom (p.12-15) ☑

1) What are the three states of matter? ☑
2) Describe the gold foil experiment carried out by Rutherford, Geiger and Marsden. ☑
3) Draw a diagram of an atom. Label the nucleus and the electrons on your diagram. ☑
4) What are isotopes? ☑

The Periodic Table and Electronic Structures (p.16-17) ☑

5) Outline how Mendeleev arranged the elements in his version of the periodic table. ☑
6) How many electrons would you expect an element in Group 7 to have in its outer shell? ☑
7) What's the maximum number of electrons that each of the first three electron shells will hold? ☑
8) The proton number of aluminium is 13. What is its electronic structure? ☑

Ionic and Covalent Bonding (p.18-20) ☑

9) What is an ion? ☑
10) Why does magnesium form ions with a 2+ charge, while sodium only forms ions with a 1+ charge? ☑
11) Explain why ionic compounds conduct electricity when they're molten, but not when they're solid. ☑
12) Describe how a covalent bond forms. ☑
13) Why do simple molecular substances have low melting and boiling points? ☑

Types of Structure (p.21-25) ☑

14) List three typical properties of giant covalent structures. ☑
15) Name three substances that have a giant covalent structure. ☑
16) What are nanoparticles? ☑
17) Name the type of molecules that plastics are made from. ☑
18) List three typical properties of metals that are due to their metallic bonding. ☑
19) Out of the four main types of structure (ionic, simple covalent, giant covalent and metallic), which one is most likely to have a low melting point? ☑

Purity and Separating Mixtures (p.26-30) ☑

20) In chemistry, what is meant by the term 'a pure substance'? ☑
21) Does adding an impurity to a substance raise or lower its boiling point? ☑
22) List the equipment that you would need to do a fractional distillation in the lab. ☑
23) What purification technique should you use to obtain a pure sample of a soluble solid from a solution? ☑
24) In chromatography, what do the terms 'mobile phase' and 'stationary phase' mean? ☑
25) Describe the method for separating a mixture by thin-layer chromatography. ☑
26) How do you calculate the R_f value of a substance from a chromatogram? ☑

Relative Masses and Formulas (p.31-32) ☑

27) What is the 'relative atomic mass' of an element? ☑
28) How do you work out the relative formula mass of a compound? ☑
29) What is the empirical formula of a compound? ☑

Topic C2 — Elements, Compounds and Mixtures

Conservation of Mass

Being a diva, I prefer the conservation of sass. <u>Conservation of mass</u> is more useful in science exams though.

In a Chemical Reaction, Mass is Always Conserved

1) During a chemical reaction <u>no atoms are destroyed</u> and <u>no atoms are created</u>.

2) This means there are the <u>same number and types of atoms</u> on each side of a reaction equation.

3) Because of this no mass is lost or gained — we say that mass is <u>conserved</u> during a reaction. <u>Example</u>: $2Li + F_2 \rightarrow 2LiF$. There are <u>2</u> lithium atoms and <u>2</u> fluorine atoms on <u>each side</u> of the equation.

4) By adding up the <u>relative masses</u> (see page 31) on each side of the equation you can see that mass is conserved.

 **EXAMPLE:** Use relative formula masses to show that mass is conserved in the following reaction: $2Li + F_2 \rightarrow 2LiF$

1) Work out the <u>total</u> of the <u>relative formula masses</u> of the <u>reactants</u>.
M_r reactants $= 2 \times M_r(Li) + M_r(F_2)$
$= (2 \times 6.9) + (2 \times 19.0) = 51.8$

2) Work out the <u>total</u> of the <u>relative formula masses</u> of the <u>products</u>.
M_r products $= 2 \times M_r(LiF)$
$= 2 \times (6.9 + 19.0) = 51.8$

3) <u>Compare</u> the total <u>relative formula masses</u> of the reactants and products.
M_r products $= 51.8$ M_r reactants $= 51.8$
So M_r reactants $= M_r$ products

There's more about balanced symbol equations on page 36.

I have literally no idea what I'm doing.

If the Mass Seems to Change, There's Usually a Gas Involved

In some experiments, you might observe a <u>change of mass</u> of an <u>unsealed reaction vessel</u> during a reaction. There are two reasons why this happens:

1 If the mass <u>increases</u>, it's probably because at least one of the <u>reactants</u> is a <u>gas</u> that's found in air (e.g. oxygen) and the products are solids, liquids or aqueous.

- <u>Before</u> the reaction, the gas is floating around in the air. It's there, but it's not contained in the reaction vessel, so you <u>can't</u> account for its <u>mass</u>.

- When the gas <u>reacts</u> to form part of the <u>product</u>, it becomes contained inside the reaction vessel.

- So the total mass of the stuff <u>inside</u> the reaction vessel increases.

- For example, when a metal reacts with oxygen in an unsealed container, the mass inside the container <u>increases</u>. The mass of the metal oxide produced equals the total mass of the <u>metal</u> and the <u>oxygen</u> that reacted from the air.
metal$_{(s)}$ + oxygen$_{(g)} \rightarrow$ metal oxide$_{(s)}$

2 If the mass <u>decreases</u>, it's probably because some, or all, of the reactants are solids, liquids or aqueous and at least one of the <u>products</u> is a <u>gas</u>.

- <u>Before</u> the reaction, any solid, liquid or aqueous reactants are contained in the reaction vessel.

- If the vessel <u>isn't enclosed</u>, then the gas can <u>escape</u> from the reaction vessel as it's formed. It's no longer contained in the reaction vessel, so you <u>can't</u> account for its <u>mass</u>.

- So the total mass of the stuff <u>inside</u> the reaction vessel <u>decreases</u>.

- For example, when a metal carbonate thermally decomposes to form a metal oxide and carbon dioxide gas, the mass of the reaction vessel will appear to <u>decrease</u> if it isn't sealed as the carbon dioxide escapes. But in reality, the mass of the <u>metal oxide</u> and the <u>carbon dioxide</u> produced will equal the mass of the metal carbonate that reacted.
metal carbonate$_{(s)} \rightarrow$ metal oxide$_{(s)}$ + carbon dioxide$_{(g)}$

Remember the particle model on page 12. A gas will expand to fill any container it's in. So if the reaction vessel isn't sealed the gas expands out from the vessel, and escapes into the air around.

Conservation of Mass — protecting mass for future generations...

Never, ever forget that, in a reaction, the total mass of reactants is the same as the total mass of products.

Q1   Using the balanced equation, show that mass is conserved in the following reaction:

$H_2SO_{4(aq)} + 2NaOH_{(aq)} \rightarrow Na_2SO_{4(aq)} + 2H_2O_{(l)}$

[3 marks]

Chemical Formulas

Make sure you've really got your head around the idea of <u>ionic bonding</u> (pages 18-19) before you start this.

You Need to be Familiar with Some Common Ions

1) You met <u>ions</u> back on page 18. They form when atoms, or groups of atoms, lose or gain electrons.

2) Here are some common ions you may meet throughout the course.
Sometimes you can <u>predict</u> the charge from where they are in the periodic table.
Others, e.g. the ions made up of more than one atom, you just have to learn.

Positive Ions		Negative Ions	
1+ ions	2+ ions	2– ions	1– ions
Lithium, Li^+	Magnesium, Mg^{2+}	Carbonate, CO_3^{2-}	Hydroxide, OH^-
Sodium, Na^+	Calcium, Ca^{2+}	Sulfate, SO_4^{2-}	Nitrate, NO_3^-
Potassium, K^+		Oxide, O^{2-}	Fluoride, F^-
		Sulfide, S^{2-}	Chloride, Cl^-
			Bromide, Br^-
			Iodide, I^-

Look back at page 18 for how to predict what ion an element will form from its position in the periodic table.

3) Any of the positive ions above can <u>combine</u> with any of the negative ions to form an <u>ionic compound</u> (see pages 18-19). For example, Na and Cl form NaCl, where sodium becomes a <u>positive ion</u> and chlorine becomes a <u>negative ion</u>.

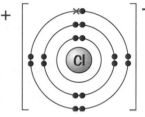

You Can Work Out the Formula of an Ionic Compound

1) Ionic compounds are made up of a <u>positively charged</u> part and a <u>negatively charged</u> part.

2) The <u>overall charge</u> of <u>any compound</u> is <u>zero</u>. So all the <u>negative charges</u> in the compound must <u>balance</u> all the <u>positive charges</u>.

3) You can use the charges on the <u>individual ions</u> present to work out the formula for the ionic compound.

4) You need to be able to write formulas using <u>chemical symbols</u>.

EXAMPLE: What is the chemical formula of calcium nitrate?

1) Write out the <u>formulas</u> for the calcium and nitrate ions. Ca^{2+}, NO_3^-

2) The <u>overall charge</u> on the formula must be <u>zero</u>, so work out the ratio of Ca : NO_3 that gives an overall neutral charge.

To balance the 2+ charge on Ca^{2+}, you need two NO_3^- ions. So formula = $Ca(NO_3)_2$

The brackets show you need two of the whole nitrate ion.

$(+2) + (2 \times -1) = 0$

You Need to Learn the Formulas of Some Molecules

1) <u>Prefixes</u> can tell you how many of a certain atom are in a molecule. The main ones you'll need to know are <u>mono-</u> = one, <u>di-</u> = two and <u>tri-</u> = three. E.g. each molecule of carbon <u>mon</u>oxide contains <u>one</u> oxygen atom and each molecule of carbon <u>di</u>oxide contains <u>two</u> oxygen atoms.

2) It's a good idea to <u>learn</u> the chemical formulas of these common molecules. They crop up all the time.

- Water — H_2O
- Ammonia — NH_3
- Carbon dioxide — CO_2
- Hydrogen — H_2
- Chlorine — Cl_2
- Oxygen — O_2

These three molecules are all called <u>diatomic</u> molecules, as they contain <u>two</u> atoms.

tricycle   dicycle   monocycle

Group 1 ions — positively wonderful, but for a small charge...

Chemical formulas pop up everywhere. Make sure you can write 'em or you'll be stumped in the exam.

Q1   Write the formula, with the charge, of the following ions:
   a) bromide ion,   b) carbonate ion,   c) lithium ion,   d) nitrate ion.   [4 marks]

Q2   What is the chemical formula of magnesium hydroxide?   [1 mark]

Chemical Equations

If you're going to get anywhere in chemistry you need to know about <u>chemical equations</u>...

Chemical Changes are Shown Using Chemical Equations

One way to show a chemical reaction is to write a <u>word equation</u>. It's not as <u>useful</u> as using chemical symbols because you can't tell straight away <u>what's happened</u> to each of the <u>atoms</u>, but it's <u>dead easy</u>.

Here's an example — <u>methane</u> burns in <u>oxygen</u> giving <u>carbon dioxide</u> and <u>water</u>:

The molecules on the <u>left-hand side</u> of the equation are called the <u>reactants</u> (because they react with each other).

$$methane + oxygen \rightarrow carbon\ dioxide + water$$

The molecules on the <u>right-hand side</u> are called the <u>products</u> (because they've been produced from the reactants).

Symbol Equations Show the Atoms on Both Sides

Chemical <u>changes</u> can be shown in a kind of <u>shorthand</u> using symbol equations. Symbol equations just show the <u>symbols or formulas</u> of the <u>reactants</u> and <u>products</u>...

magnesium + oxygen		magnesium oxide
$2Mg$ + O_2	$\rightarrow$	$2MgO$

The numbers in front of the formulas show the ratios between the number of moles of each substance (see pages 38-40 for more on moles and equations).

Symbol Equations Need to be Balanced

1) There must always be the <u>same</u> number of atoms on <u>both sides</u> of the equation — they can't just <u>disappear</u>.

2) You <u>balance</u> the equation by putting numbers <u>in front</u> of the formulas where needed. Take this equation for reacting sulfuric acid with sodium hydroxide:

$$H_2SO_4 + NaOH \rightarrow Na_2SO_4 + H_2O$$

3) The <u>formulas</u> are all correct but the numbers of some atoms <u>don't match up</u> on both sides.

4) You <u>can't change formulas</u> like H_2SO_4 to H_2SO_5. You can only put numbers <u>in front of them</u>.

The more you <u>practise</u>, the <u>quicker</u> you get, but all you do is this:

$E=mc^2$

- Find an element that <u>doesn't balance</u> and <u>pencil in a number</u> to try and sort it out.
- <u>See where it gets you</u>. It may create <u>another imbalance</u>, but if so, pencil in <u>another number</u> and see where that gets you.
- Carry on chasing <u>unbalanced</u> elements and the equation will <u>sort itself out</u> pretty quickly.

EXAMPLE: In the equation above you'll notice we're short of <u>H atoms</u> on the RHS (Right-Hand Side).

1) The only thing you can do about that is make it <u>2H₂O</u> instead of just H_2O:
$$H_2SO_4 + NaOH \rightarrow Na_2SO_4 + 2H_2O$$

2) But that now gives <u>too many</u> H atoms and O atoms on the RHS, so to balance that up you could try putting <u>2NaOH</u> on the LHS (Left-Hand Side):
$$H_2SO_4 + 2NaOH \rightarrow Na_2SO_4 + 2H_2O$$

3) And suddenly there it is! <u>Everything balances</u>. And you'll notice the Na just sorted itself out.

Revision is all about getting the balance right...

Balancing equations is all about practice. Once you have a few goes you'll see it's much less scary than it seemed before you took on, challenged and defeated this page. Go grab some chemistry glory.

Q1   Balance the equation: $Fe + Cl_2 \rightarrow FeCl_3$ [1 mark]

Q2   Hydrogen and oxygen molecules are formed in a reaction where water splits apart.
       For this reaction: a) State the word equation.   b) Give a balanced symbol equation.   [3 marks]

More on Chemical Equations

If you thought that was all there was to know about <u>chemical equations</u>, prepare to be sorely disappointed...

State Symbols Tell You the State of a Substance in an Equation

You saw on the last page how a chemical reaction can be shown using a <u>word equation</u> or a <u>symbol equation</u>. Symbol equations can also include <u>state symbols</u> next to each substance — they tell you what <u>physical state</u> (see page 12) the reactants and products are in:

> (s) — solid   (l) — liquid   (g) — gas   (aq) — aqueous

'Aqueous' means 'dissolved in water'.

> <u>Example</u>: Aqueous hydrochloric acid reacts with solid calcium carbonate to form aqueous calcium chloride, liquid water and carbon dioxide gas: $2HCl_{(aq)} + CaCO_{3(s)} \rightarrow CaCl_{2(aq)} + H_2O_{(l)} + CO_{2(g)}$

Ionic Equations Show Just the Useful Bits of Reactions

1) You can also write an <u>ionic equation</u> for any reaction involving ions that happens in solution.

2) In an ionic equation, only the <u>reacting particles</u> (and the products they form) are included.

3) To write an ionic equation, you've just got to look at the reactants and products. Anything that's <u>exactly the same</u> on <u>both sides</u> of the equation can be left out.

 **EXAMPLE:** Write the ionic equation for the following reaction:
$$CaCl_{2\,(aq)} + 2NaOH_{(aq)} \rightarrow Ca(OH)_{2\,(s)} + 2NaCl_{(aq)}$$

You should make sure your symbol equation is balanced before you start trying to write the ionic equation (see the last page for more on how to balance symbol equations).

1) Anything that's <u>ionic</u> (i.e. made of ions — see page 18) and aqueous will break up into its ions in solution. So, write out the equation showing all the <u>ions separately</u>.
$$Ca^{2+}_{(aq)} + 2Cl^-_{(aq)} + 2Na^+_{(aq)} + 2OH^-_{(aq)} \rightarrow Ca(OH)_{2\,(s)} + 2Na^+_{(aq)} + 2Cl^-_{(aq)}$$

2) To get to the ionic equation, <u>cross out</u> anything that's the <u>same on both sides</u> of the equation — here, those are the Na^+ and Cl^- ions.
$$Ca^{2+}_{(aq)} + 2\cancel{Cl^-}_{(aq)} + 2\cancel{Na^+}_{(aq)} + 2OH^-_{(aq)} \rightarrow Ca(OH)_{2\,(s)} + 2\cancel{Na^+}_{(aq)} + 2\cancel{Cl^-}_{(aq)}$$
$$Ca^{2+}_{(aq)} + 2OH^-_{(aq)} \rightarrow Ca(OH)_{2\,(s)}$$

The overall charge should be the same on both sides of the reaction.

Half Equations Show the Movement of Electrons

<u>Half equations</u> show how electrons are transferred during reactions. In half equations, e^- stands for <u>one electron</u>.

You can't write half equations for all chemical reactions — only the ones where <u>oxidation</u> or <u>reduction</u> happen (see page 47).

Half equations are really useful for showing what happens at each electrode during electrolysis (see page 47-49).

> <u>Examples</u>: In this half equation, sodium is losing one electron to become a sodium ion.
> $$Na \rightarrow Na^+ + e^-$$
> In this equation, two hydrogen ions are each gaining one electron to form a hydrogen molecule.
> $$2H^+ + 2e^- \rightarrow H_2$$

The charges on each side of the equation should balance.

You can <u>combine half equations</u> to create <u>full ionic equations</u>.
Full equations <u>never</u> contain electrons — the electrons in the reactants and products should <u>cancel out</u>.
So, in the sodium/hydrogen example above, the <u>full ionic equation</u> would be: $2Na + 2H^+ \rightarrow 2Na^+ + H_2$.
(You need to multiply the sodium half equation by 2 so the electrons on each side balance.)

Half equations — equa, equa, equa, equa, equa, equa...

They may be half equations, but they're double the trouble if you ask me. Better get some practice in...

Q1   Write the ionic equation for the following reaction: $HNO_{3\,(aq)} + NaOH_{(aq)} \rightarrow NaNO_{3\,(aq)} + H_2O_{(l)}$ [1 mark]

Q2   Write a half equation to show a chlorine molecule gaining electrons to become chloride ions.   [2 marks]

Moles

The mole might seem a bit confusing. I think it's the word that puts people off. But it's not that hard really...

"The Mole" is Simply the Name Given to a Certain Number

1) Just like a million is this many: 1 000 000, or a billion is this many: 1 000 000 000, a mole is given by Avogadro's constant, and it's this many: 602 200 000 000 000 000 000 000 or 6.022×10^{23}.

2) But what does Avogadro's constant show? The answer is that when you get that number of atoms or molecules, of any element or compound, then, conveniently, they weigh exactly the same number of grams as the relative atomic mass, A_r (or relative formula mass, M_r) of the element or compound.

> One mole of atoms or molecules of any substance will have a mass in grams equal to the relative formula mass (A_r or M_r) for that substance.

Look back at page 31 if you've forgotten how to work out A_r and M_r.

Examples:

Carbon has an A_r of 12.   So one mole of carbon weighs exactly 12 g.

Nitrogen gas, N_2, has an M_r of 28 (2×14).   So one mole of nitrogen gas weighs exactly 28 g.

Hexane, C_6H_{14}, has an M_r of 86 ((6×12) + (14×1)).   So one mole of hexane weighs exactly 86 g.

So 12 g of carbon, 28 g of nitrogen gas and 86 g of hexane all contain the same number of particles, namely one mole or 6.022×10^{23} particles.

EXAMPLE: How many atoms are there in 5 moles of oxygen gas?

1) Multiply Avogadro's constant by the number of moles you have to find the number of particles.

$$6.022 \times 10^{23} \times 5 = 3.011 \times 10^{24}$$

2) There are two atoms in each molecule of oxygen gas, so multiply your answer by 2.

$$3.011 \times 10^{24} \times 2 = 6.022 \times 10^{24}$$

Give your answer in standard form (in terms of $\times 10^x$) to save you having to write out lots of 0's.

3) To find the mass of an atom of a certain element, just divide its relative atomic mass by Avogadro's constant.

EXAMPLE: What is the mean mass of one atom of iron?

Mass of one atom = A_r ÷ Avogadro's constant
$$= 55.8 \div (6.022 \times 10^{23}) = 9.27 \times 10^{-23} \text{ g}$$

You Can Find the Number of Moles in a Given Mass

There's a nifty formula you can use to find the number of moles in a certain mass of something. You need to know how to use it, and be able to rearrange it to find mass or M_r.

You can rearrange an equation using a formula triangle. Just cover the thing you want to find, and you're left the expression you need to calculate it.

$$\text{Number of Moles} = \frac{\text{Mass in g (of element or compound)}}{M_r \text{ (of element or compound)}}$$

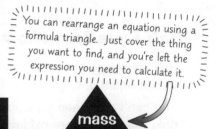

To find the number of moles of atoms in a certain mass of an element, just replace M_r in the formula with A_r.

EXAMPLE: How many moles are there in 66 g of carbon dioxide?

M_r of carbon dioxide (CO_2) = $12.0 + (2 \times 16.0) = 44.0$

moles = mass ÷ M_r = $66 \div 44.0$ = 1.5 moles

EXAMPLE: What mass of carbon is there in 4.0 moles of carbon dioxide?

mass = moles × A_r
$= 4.0 \times 12.0 = 44$ g

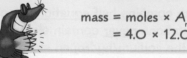

What do moles do for fun? Moller skate...

Moles can give you a bit of a headache — so spend a bit of time getting your head round all this if you need to.

Q1   Calculate the number of moles in 90 g of water. M_r of water = 18.0.   [1 mark]

Q2   Calculate the mass of 0.200 moles of potassium bromide. M_r of KBr = 119.0.   [1 mark]

Q3   0.500 moles of substance X has a mass of 87.0 g. What is the relative formula mass of X?   [1 mark]

Calculating Masses

Unlimited. Together we're unlimited. Unless you're a limiting reactant, in which case you're a big ol' limiter.

Reactions Stop When One Reactant is Used Up

1) A reaction stops when all of one of the reactants is used up. Any other reactants are said to be in excess.

2) The reactant that's used up in a reaction is called the limiting reactant (because it limits the amount of product that's formed).

3) The amount of product formed is directly proportional to the amount of limiting reactant. This is because if you add more of the limiting reactant there will be more reactant particles to take part in the reaction, which means more product particles are made (as long as the other reactants are in excess).

The Amount of Product Depends on the Limiting Reactant

You can use a balanced chemical equation to work out the mass of product formed from a given mass of a limiting reactant. Here's how...

> You could also use this method to find the mass of a reactant needed to produce a known mass of a product.

1) Write out the balanced equation.

2) Work out relative formula masses (M_r) of the reactant and product you want.

3) Find out how many moles there are of the substance you know the mass of.

4) Use the balanced equation to work out how many moles there'll be of the other substance (i.e. how many moles of product will be made by this many moles of reactant).

5) Use the number of moles to calculate the mass.

EXAMPLE: Calculate the mass of aluminium oxide formed when 135 g of aluminium is burned in air.

1) Write out the balanced equation:
$$4Al + 3O_2 \rightarrow 2Al_2O_3$$

2) Calculate the relative atomic or formula masses of the reactants and products you're interested in.
Al: 27 Al_2O_3: $(2 \times 27.0) + (3 \times 16.0) = 102.0$

3) Calculate the number of moles of aluminium in 135 g:
moles = mass ÷ M_r = 135 ÷ 27.0 = 5

4) Look at the ratio of moles in the equation:
4 moles of Al react to produce 2 moles of Al_2O_3 — half the number of moles are produced. So 5 moles of Al will react to produce 2.5 moles of Al_2O_3.

5) Calculate the mass of 2.5 moles of aluminium oxide:
mass = moles × M_r = 2.5 × 102.0 = **255 g**

EXAMPLE: Magnesium oxide can be made by burning magnesium in air. What mass of magnesium is needed to make 100 g of magnesium oxide?

1) Write out the balanced equation.
$$2Mg + O_2 \rightarrow 2MgO$$

2) Work out the relative atomic or formula masses of the reactants and products you're interested in.
Mg: 24.3   MgO: 24.3 + 16.0 = 40.3

3) Calculate the number of moles of magnesium oxide in 100 g:
moles = mass ÷ M_r = 100 ÷ 40.3 = 2.48...

4) Look at the ratio of moles in the equation to work out the no. moles of reactant used, compared to the no. moles of product made.
2 moles of MgO are made from 2 moles of Mg. So 2.48... moles of MgO will be formed from 2.48... moles of Mg.

5) Calculate the mass of 2.5 moles of Mg.
mass = moles × M_r = 2.48... × 24.3 = **60.3 g**

Relative mass — when you go to church with your parents...

A specially organically grown, hand-picked question for you my dear. Don't say I don't spoil you.

Q1 Chlorine and potassium bromide react according to this equation: $Cl_2 + 2KBr \rightarrow Br_2 + 2KCl$
Calculate the mass of bromine produced when 23.8 g of potassium bromide reacts in an excess of chlorine.

[4 marks]

More Mole Calculations

You've already seen how to balance equations back on page 36. But, sometimes, you may have to balance equations given the masses of the reactants and products. Your good old friend the mole will come in handy...

You Can Balance Equations Using Reacting Masses

If you know the masses of the reactants and products that took part in a reaction, you can work out the balanced symbol equation for the reaction. Here are the steps you should take:

1) Divide the mass of each substance by its relative formula mass to find the number of moles.

   You may need to work out some unknown masses first (see below).

2) Divide the number of moles of each substance by the smallest number of moles in the reaction.

3) If needed, multiply all the numbers by the same amount to make them all whole numbers.

4) Write the balanced symbol equation for the reaction by putting these numbers in front of the formulas.

EXAMPLE:

Paula burns a metal, X, in oxygen. There is a single product, an oxide of the metal. Given that 25.4 g of X burns in 3.2 g of oxygen, write a balanced equation for this reaction. A_r of X = 63.5 and M_r of X oxide = 143.0.

1) Work out the mass of metal oxide produced. Because it's the only product, the mass of metal oxide produced must equal the total mass of reactants. $25.4 + 3.2 = 28.6$ g of X oxide

2) Divide the mass of each substance by its M_r or A_r to calculate how many moles of each substance reacted or were produced:

   X: $\frac{25.4}{63.5} = 0.40$ mol O_2: $\frac{3.2}{32.0} = 0.10$ mol   X oxide: $\frac{28.6}{143.0} = 0.20$ mol

3) Divide by the smallest number of moles, which is 0.10:   X: $\frac{0.40}{0.10} = 4.0$ O_2: $\frac{0.10}{0.10} = 1.0$ X oxide: $\frac{0.20}{0.10} = 2.0$

4) The numbers are all whole numbers, so you can write out the balanced symbol equation straight away. $4X + O_2 \rightarrow 2(X \text{ oxide})$

5) The oxide of X must have a chemical formula containing X and O atoms. In order for the equation to balance, each molecule of X oxide must contain one O atom and 2 X atoms. $4X + O_2 \rightarrow 2X_2O$

You Can Work Out Limiting Reactants

EXAMPLE:

8.14 g of zinc oxide (ZnO) were put in a crucible with 0.30 g of carbon and heated until they reacted. Given that the balanced chemical equation for this reaction is: $2ZnO + C \rightarrow CO_2 + 2Zn$, work out the limiting reactant in this reaction.

1) Divide the mass of each substance by its M_r or A_r to find how many moles of each substance were reacted: ZnO: $\frac{8.14}{81.4} = 0.10$ mol   C: $\frac{0.30}{12.0} = 0.025$ mol

2) Divide by the smallest number of moles, which is 0.025:   ZnO: $\frac{0.10}{0.025} = 4.0$ C: $\frac{0.025}{0.025} = 1.0$

3) Compare the ratios between the moles of products with the balanced chemical equation.   In the balanced equation, ZnO and C react in a ratio of 2 : 1. Using the masses, there is a 4 : 1 ratio of ZnO to C. So, ZnO is in excess, and C must be the limiting reactant.

What do moles have for pudding? Jam moly-poly...

The best way to get to grips with the maths on this page is by practising. Luckily for you, there is a fine looking question below to get you started. Don't say I don't spoil you. Better get cracking...

Q1   84 g of nitrogen gas are sealed in a vessel with 12 g of hydrogen gas and heated. They react to produce ammonia. The equation for the reaction is: $N_2 + 3H_2 \rightarrow 2NH_3$. What is the limiting reactant?   [3 marks]

Endothermic and Exothermic Reactions

Whenever chemical reactions occur, there are changes in <u>energy</u>. This is kind of interesting if you think of the number of chemical reactions that are involved in everyday life.

Combustion reactions (where something burns in oxygen) are always exothermic.

Reactions are Exothermic or Endothermic

An <u>EXOTHERMIC reaction</u> is one which <u>gives out energy</u> to the surroundings, usually in the form of <u>heat</u> and usually shown by a <u>rise in temperature</u> of the surroundings.

An <u>ENDOTHERMIC reaction</u> is one which <u>takes in energy</u> from the surroundings, usually in the form of <u>heat</u> and usually shown by a <u>fall in temperature</u> of the surroundings.

Reaction Profiles Show if a Reaction's Exo- or Endothermic

<u>Reaction profiles</u> show the energy levels of the <u>reactants</u> and the <u>products</u> in a reaction. You can use them to work out if energy is <u>released</u> (exothermic) or <u>taken in</u> (endothermic).

1) This shows an <u>exothermic reaction</u> — the products are at a <u>lower energy</u> than the reactants.

2) The <u>difference in height</u> represents the <u>energy given out</u> in the reaction.

EXOTHERMIC

Energy

Reactants

Energy is released

Products

Progress of reaction

ENDOTHERMIC

Energy

Products

Energy is absorbed

Reactants

Progress of reaction

3) This shows an <u>endothermic reaction</u> because the products are at a <u>higher energy</u> than the reactants.

4) The <u>difference in height</u> represents the <u>energy taken in</u> during the reaction.

Activation Energy is the Energy Needed to Start a Reaction

1) The <u>activation energy</u> is the <u>minimum</u> amount of energy needed for <u>bonds to break</u> (see next page) and a reaction to start.

2) On a reaction profile, it's the energy difference between the reactants and the highest point on the curve.

3) It's a bit like having to <u>climb up</u> one side of a hill before you can ski/snowboard/sledge/fall down the <u>other side</u>.

4) If the <u>energy input is less than</u> the activation energy there <u>won't</u> be enough energy to <u>start</u> the reaction — so nothing will happen.

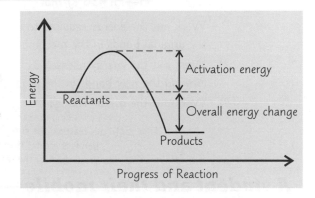

Exothermic reactions are a hot topic right now...

Remember, "exo-" = exit, "-thermic" = heat, so an exothermic reaction is one that gives out heat — and endothermic means just the opposite. To make sure you really understand these terms, try this question.

Q1   The temperature of a reaction mixture increases from 21 °C to 28.5 °C over the course of the reaction.
  a)   Is the reaction exothermic or endothermic?   [1 mark]
  b)   Sketch a reaction profile to show the reaction. Label the energy of the reactants,
        the energy of the products and the activation energy.
                                                                                                      [3 marks]

Bond Energies

Energy transfer in chemical reactions is all to do with <u>making and breaking bonds</u>.

Energy Must Always be Supplied to Break Bonds

1) During a chemical reaction, <u>old bonds are broken</u> and <u>new bonds are formed</u>.

2) Energy must be <u>supplied</u> to break <u>existing bonds</u> — so bond breaking is an <u>endothermic</u> process.

3) Energy is <u>released</u> when new bonds are <u>formed</u> — so bond formation is an <u>exothermic</u> process.

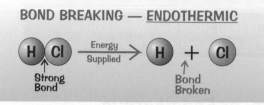

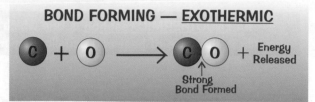

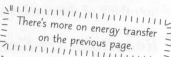

There's more on energy transfer on the previous page.

4) In <u>endothermic</u> reactions, the energy <u>used</u> to break bonds is <u>greater</u> than the energy <u>released</u> by forming them.

5) In <u>exothermic</u> reactions, the energy <u>released</u> by forming bonds is <u>greater</u> than the energy used to <u>break</u> 'em.

Bond Energy Calculations — Need to be Practised

1) <u>Every</u> chemical bond has a particular <u>bond energy</u> associated with it. This <u>bond energy</u> varies slightly depending on the <u>compound</u> the bond occurs in.

2) You can use these <u>known bond energies</u> to calculate the <u>overall energy change</u> for a reaction.

Overall Energy Change	=	Energy required to break bonds	−	Energy released by forming bonds

3) A <u>positive</u> energy change means an <u>endothermic</u> reaction and a <u>negative</u> energy change means an <u>exothermic</u> reaction.

4) You need to <u>practise</u> a few of these, but the basic idea is really very simple...

EXAMPLE: Using the bond energy values below, calculate the energy change for the following reaction, where hydrogen and chlorine react to produce hydrogen chloride:

$$H—H + Cl—Cl \rightarrow 2H—Cl$$

H—H: 436 kJ/mol   Cl—Cl: 242 kJ/mol   H—Cl: 431 kJ/mol

1) Work out the energy required to break the <u>original bonds</u> in the reactants.

$(1 \times H—H) + (1 \times Cl—Cl) = 436 + 242$
$= 678$ kJ/mol

2) Work out the energy released by forming the <u>new bonds</u> in the products.

$(2 \times H—Cl) = 2 \times 431$
$= 862$ kJ/mol

3) Work out the overall change.

overall energy change = energy required to break bonds − energy released by forming bonds

$= 678 − 862 = −184$ kJ/mol

In this reaction, the energy released by forming bonds is greater than the energy used to break them so the reaction is exothermic.

A student and their mobile — a bond that can never be broken...

This stuff might look hard at the moment, but with a bit of practice it's dead easy and it'll win you easy marks if you understand all the theory behind it. See how you get on with this question:

Q1 During the Haber Process, N_2 reacts with H_2 in the following reaction: $N_2 + 3H_2 \rightleftharpoons 2NH_3$

The bond energies for these molecules are:
N≡N: 941 kJ/mol, H–H: 436 kJ/mol,
N–H: 391 kJ/mol.
Calculate the overall energy change
for the forward reaction, shown on the right.

N≡N + H–H ⟶ N with H H and N with H H
       H–H
       H–H

[3 marks]

Acids and Bases

Testing the pH of a solution means using an <u>indicator</u> — and that means pretty <u>co ours</u>...

The pH Scale Goes From 0 to 14

1) The pH scale is a measure of <u>how acidic or alkaline</u> a solution is. A <u>neutral</u> substance has <u>pH 7</u>.

2) An <u>acid</u> is a substance with a <u>pH less than 7</u>. Acids form H^+ ions in water.

3) A <u>base</u> is a substance with a <u>pH greater than 7</u>.
An <u>alkali</u> is a base that <u>dissolves in water</u>. Alkalis form OH^- ions in water.

OH^- ions are called hydroxide ions.

4) The value of the pH is <u>inversely proportional</u> to the <u>concentration of hydrogen ions</u> in a solution.
So, as the concentration of hydrogen ions <u>increases</u>, the <u>pH decreases</u>. This makes sense, because the higher the hydrogen ion concentration, the <u>more acidic</u> something is, so the lower the pH.

You Can Measure the pH of a Solution

PRACTICAL

An <u>indicator</u> is a <u>dye</u> that <u>changes colour</u> depending on whether it's <u>above or below</u> a certain pH. <u>Universal indicator</u> is a <u>combination of dyes</u>. It's very useful for <u>estimating</u> the pH of a solution. Indicators are simple to use — <u>add a few drops</u> to the solution you're testing, then compare the colour the solution goes to a <u>pH chart</u> for that indicator. Here's a pH chart for Universal indicator:

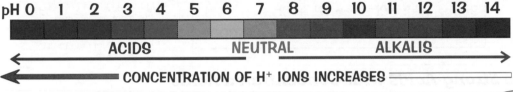

pH 0 1 2 3 4 5 6 7 8 9 10 11 12 13 14

ACIDS   NEUTRAL   ALKALIS

CONCENTRATION OF H^+ IONS INCREASES

A <u>pH probe</u> attached to a <u>pH meter</u> can be used to measure pH <u>electronically</u>. The probe is placed in the solution you are measuring and the pH is given on a digital display as a <u>numerical value</u>. This gives a <u>higher level</u> of accuracy than an indicator. When using a pH probe, it's important you <u>calibrate it correctly</u> (by setting it to read pH 7 in a sample of pure water), and rinse the probe with deionised water in between readings.

Acids and Bases Neutralise Each Other

The reaction between acids and bases is called <u>neutralisation</u>. It produces a <u>salt</u> and <u>water</u> (see page 45 for more on this).

$$HCl + NaOH \rightarrow NaCl + H_2O$$
acid   base   salt   water

Neutralisation reactions in <u>aqueous solution</u> can also be shown as an ionic equation (see p.37) in terms of <u>H^+</u> and <u>OH^-</u> ions:

$$H^+_{(aq)} + OH^-_{(aq)} \rightarrow H_2O_{(l)}$$

This is just the ionic equation of the reaction above.

When an acid neutralises a base (or vice versa), the <u>products</u> are <u>neutral</u>, i.e. they have a <u>pH of 7</u>. At pH 7, the concentration of hydrogen ions equals the concentration of hydroxide ions. An indicator can be used to show that a neutralisation reaction is over (Universal indicator will go green).

Titration Curves Show pH Changes with Volume

1) Titrations (see page 64) are used to work out how much of an acid is used to <u>neutralise</u> a base of unknown concentration (or vice versa).

2) <u>Titration curves</u> are used to show where <u>neutralisation</u> happens during a titration. There's a <u>vertical point</u> in the curve which is where the solution is <u>neutral</u> (at pH 7). This is called the <u>end point</u> of the titration.

If you add acid to a base, the pH will decrease. If you add a base to an acid, then the pH will increase.

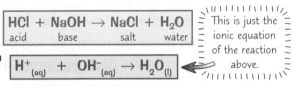

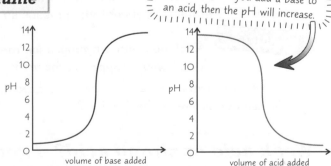

volume of base added   volume of acid added

This page should have all bases covered...

pHew, you got to the end of the page, so here's an interesting(ish) fact — your skin is slightly acidic (pH 5.5).

Q1   a) The pH of an unknown solution is found to be 6. Is the solution acidic or alkaline?   [1 mark]
     b) What colour would the solution go if a few drops of Universal indicator were added to it?   [1 mark]

Strong and Weak Acids

Right then. More on acids. Brace yourself.

Acids Produce Protons in Water

The thing about acids is that they ionise — they produce hydrogen ions, H^+.
For example,

$$HCl \rightarrow H^+ + Cl^-$$
$$HNO_3 \rightarrow H^+ + NO_3^-$$

An H^+ ion is just a proton.

HCl and HNO_3 don't produce hydrogen ions until they meet water.

Acids Can be Strong or Weak

1) Strong acids (e.g. sulfuric, hydrochloric and nitric acids) ionise almost completely in water.
   A large proportion of acid molecules dissociate to release H^+ ions. They tend to have low pHs (pH 0-2).

2) Weak acids (e.g. ethanoic, citric and carbonic acids) do not fully ionise in solution.
   Only a small proportion of acid molecules dissociate to release H^+ ions. Their pHs tend to be around 2-6.

3) The ionisation of a weak acid is a reversible reaction, which sets up an equilibrium mixture.
   Since only a few of the acid molecules release H^+ ions, the equilibrium lies well to the left.

Strong acid: $HCl \longrightarrow H^+ + Cl^-$

Weak acid: $CH_3COOH \rightleftharpoons H^+ + CH_3COO^-$

For more on equilibria turn to page 73.

Don't Confuse Strong Acids with Concentrated Acids

1) Acid strength (i.e. strong or weak) tells you what proportion of the acid molecules ionise in water.

2) The concentration of an acid is different. Concentration measures how much acid
   there is in a litre (1 dm^3) of water. Concentration is basically how watered down your acid is.

3) An acid with a high proportion of acid molecules compared to the volume of
   water is said to be concentrated. An acid with a low proportion of acid
   molecules compared to the volume of water is said to be dilute.

Concentration is measured in g/dm^3 or mol/dm^3.

4) Note that concentration describes the total number of dissolved acid molecules
   — not the number of molecules that produce hydrogen ions.

5) The more grams (or moles) of acid per dm^3, the more concentrated the acid is.

6) So you can have a dilute but strong acid, or a concentrated but weak acid.

Changing the Concentration of an Acid Affects its pH

If the concentration of H^+ ions increases by a factor of 10, the pH decreases by 1. So if the H^+ ion
concentration increases by a factor of 100 (= 10 × 10), the pH decreases by 2 (= 1 + 1), and so on.
Decreasing the H^+ ion concentration has the opposite effect — a decrease by
a factor of 10 in the H^+ concentration means an increase of 1 on the pH scale.

EXAMPLE:

A solution with a hydrogen ion concentration of 0.001 mol/dm^3 has a pH of 4.
What would happen to the pH if you increased the hydrogen ion concentration to 0.01 mol/dm^3?

The H^+ concentration has increased by a factor of 10, so the pH would decrease by 1.
So the new pH would be 4 − 1 = 3.

Weak acid or strong acid? I know which goes better with chips...

Acids are acidic because of H^+ ions. And strong acids are strong because they let go of all their H^+ ions at the drop
of a hat... Well, at the drop of a drop of water.

Q1 Explain the difference between a strong acid and a weak acid. [2 marks]

Q2 A student added strong acid to a weakly acidic solution of pH 6. The pH of the new solution
was found to be pH 3. By how many times did the concentration of H^+ increase or decrease? [2 marks]

Reactions of Acids

MORE? You want MORE? Well, I'm much kinder than a Dickensian orphanage master, so <u>more acids</u> for you.

Many Metals React With Acids to Give Salts

$$Acid + Metal \rightarrow Salt + Hydrogen$$

A salt is an ionic compound, formed as part of a neutralisation reaction.

Hydrochloric Acid Produces Chloride Salts:
$2HCl + Mg \rightarrow MgCl_2 + H_2$ (Magnesium chloride)
$6HCl + 2Al \rightarrow 2AlCl_3 + 3H_2$ (Aluminium chloride)

Sulfuric Acid Produces Sulfate Salts:
$H_2SO_4 + Mg \rightarrow MgSO_4 + H_2$ (Magnesium sulfate)
$3H_2SO_4 + 2Al \rightarrow Al_2(SO_4)_3 + 3H_2$ (Aluminium sulfate)

Nitric Acid Produces Nitrate Salts When NEUTRALISED, But...

The reaction of nitric acid with metals is more complicated — you get a nitrate salt, but instead of hydrogen gas, the other products are usually a mixture of water, NO and NO_2.

You can't really predict the balanced equation for the reaction of nitric acid with metals.

Metal Carbonates Give Salt + Water + Carbon Dioxide

$$Acid + Metal\ Carbonate \rightarrow Salt + Water + Carbon\ Dioxide$$

<u>Examples:</u> $2HCl + Na_2CO_3 \rightarrow 2NaCl + H_2O + CO_2$ (Sodium chloride)
$H_2SO_4 + K_2CO_3 \rightarrow K_2SO_4 + H_2O + CO_2$ (Potassium sulfate)
$2HNO_3 + ZnCO_3 \rightarrow Zn(NO_3)_2 + H_2O + CO_2$ (Zinc nitrate)

Again, as above, hydrochloric acid produces chloride salts, sulfuric acid produces sulfate salts, and nitric acid produces nitrate salts.

Acids and Alkalis React to Give a Salt and Water

$$Acid + Alkali \rightarrow Salt + Water$$

<u>Examples:</u> $HCl + NaOH \rightarrow NaCl + H_2O$ (Sodium chloride)
$H_2SO_4 + Zn(OH)_2 \rightarrow ZnSO_4 + 2H_2O$ (Zinc sulfate)
$HNO_3 + KOH \rightarrow KNO_3 + H_2O$ (Potassium nitrate)

You met neutralisation reactions back on page 43.

You can Make Soluble Salts Using Acid/Alkali Reactions

PRACTICAL

1) Soluble salts (salts that dissolve in water) can be made by reacting an acid with an <u>alkali</u>.

2) But you can't tell whether the reaction has <u>finished</u> — there's no signal that all the acid has been neutralised. You also can't just add an <u>excess</u> of alkali to the acid and filter out what's left because the salt is <u>soluble</u> and would be contaminated with the excess alkali.

3) Instead, you have to add <u>exactly</u> the right amount of alkali to <u>neutralise</u> the acid. You can carry out a <u>titration</u> (see page 64) to work out the <u>exact amount</u> of alkali needed.

4) Then, carry out the reaction using exactly the right proportions of alkali and acid but with no <u>indicator</u> (because you now know the volumes needed), so the salt <u>won't be contaminated</u> with indicator.

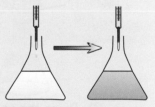

5) The <u>solution</u> that remains when the reaction is complete contains only the <u>salt</u> and <u>water</u>. Slowly <u>evaporate</u> off some of the water and then leave the solution to crystallise. Filter off the solid and dry it — you'll be left with a <u>pure</u>, <u>dry</u> salt (see page 28 for more on crystallisation).

Nitrates — much cheaper than day-rates...

What a lot of reactions. Better take a peek back at page 36 for help with writing and balancing chemical equations.

Q1   Write a balanced chemical equation for the reaction of hydrochloric acid with calcium carbonate.   [2 marks]

Making Salts

Making salts can be tricky. You need a different method depending on whether the salt's <u>insoluble</u> or <u>soluble</u>. You met one technique for making soluble salts on the last page. Time for some more...

Making Soluble Salts Using an Acid and an Insoluble Reactant

1) You can make soluble salts by reacting an acid with an insoluble base.

2) You need to pick the right <u>acid</u>, plus a <u>metal</u> or an <u>insoluble base</u> (a <u>metal oxide</u> or <u>metal hydroxide</u>).

3) Add the <u>base</u> to the <u>acid</u> — the base and acid will react to produce a <u>soluble salt</u> (and water). You will know when all the acid has been neutralised because the excess solid will just <u>sink</u> to the bottom of the flask.
You sometimes need to heat the reaction mixture during this step to get the acid and base to react.

4) Then <u>filter</u> off the <u>excess</u> solid to get a solution containing only salt and water.

5) <u>Heat the solution gently</u> to slowly <u>evaporate</u> off some of the water, then leave the more concentrated solution to cool and allow the salt to <u>crystallise</u> (see page 28). Filter off the solid and leave it to <u>dry</u>.

filter paper

filter funnel

excess solid

salt and water

> **Example:** You can add <u>copper oxide</u> to <u>hydrochloric acid</u> to make <u>copper chloride</u>:
> $$CuO_{(s)} + 2HCl_{(aq)} \rightarrow CuCl_{2(aq)} + H_2O_{(l)}$$

Making Insoluble Salts — Precipitation Reactions

1) To make a pure, dry sample of an <u>insoluble</u> salt, you can use a <u>precipitation reaction</u>. You just need to pick the right two <u>soluble salts</u>, they <u>react</u> and you get your <u>insoluble salt</u>.

2) E.g. to make <u>lead chloride</u> (insoluble), mix <u>lead nitrate</u> and <u>sodium chloride</u> (both soluble).

lead nitrate + sodium chloride → lead chloride + sodium nitrate
$$Pb(NO_3)_{2\,(aq)} + 2NaCl_{(aq)} \rightarrow PbCl_{2\,(s)} + 2NaNO_{3\,(aq)}$$

Soluble things dissolve in water. Insoluble things don't.

Method

1) Add 1 spatula of <u>lead nitrate</u> to a test tube. Add <u>deionised water</u> to dissolve the lead nitrate. Use deionised water to make sure there are no other ions about. <u>Shake it thoroughly</u> to ensure that all the lead nitrate has <u>dissolved</u>. Then, in a separate test tube, do the same with 1 spatula of <u>sodium chloride</u>.

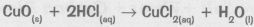

precipitate

2) Tip the <u>two solutions</u> into a small beaker, and give it a good stir to make sure it's all mixed together. The lead chloride should <u>precipitate</u> out.

3) Put a folded piece of <u>filter paper</u> into a <u>filter funnel</u>, and stick the funnel into a <u>conical flask</u>.

filter paper

filter funnel

4) <u>Pour</u> the contents of the beaker into the middle of the filter paper. Make sure that the solution doesn't go above the filter paper — otherwise some of the solid could dribble down the side.

5) <u>Swill out</u> the beaker with more deionised water, and tip this into the filter paper — to make sure you get <u>all the wanted product</u> from the beaker.

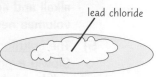

lead chloride

6) Rinse the contents of the filter paper with deionised water to make sure that <u>all the soluble sodium nitrate</u> has been washed away.

7) Then just scrape the <u>lead chloride</u> onto fresh filter paper and leave to dry.

I was attacked by a nasty lead chloride — it was a-salt...

The theory may seem dull, but you'll probably get to make some nice salts in your class, and that's pretty cool.

Q1   Iron nitrate is a soluble salt that can be made from iron oxide (an insoluble base) and nitric acid. Suggest a method you could use to make a pure sample of iron nitrate from these reactants.   [3 marks]

Oxidation and Reduction

Oxidation can be to do with something gaining oxygen (makes sense), but it can also be to do with electrons...

If Electrons are Transferred, It's a Redox Reaction

1) Oxidation can mean the reaction with, or addition of oxygen, and reduction can be the removal of oxygen.

$$Fe_2O_3 + 3CO \rightarrow 2Fe + 3CO_2$$

- Iron oxide is reduced to iron (as oxygen is removed).
- Carbon monoxide is oxidised to carbon dioxide (as oxygen is added).

Combustion reactions involve oxidation. They're always exothermic (see p.41). E.g. $CH_4 + 2O_2 \rightarrow CO_2 + 2H_2O$

2) But on this page, we're looking at oxidation and reduction in terms of electrons. A loss of electrons is called oxidation. A gain of electrons is called reduction.

3) REDuction and OXidation happen at the same time — so this type of reaction is called a redox reaction.

4) An oxidising agent accepts electrons and gets reduced (it gains electrons or loses oxygen).

5) A reducing agent donates electrons and gets oxidised (it loses electrons or gains oxygen).

When dealing with electrons:
Oxidation Is Loss,
Reduction Is Gain.
Remember it as OIL RIG.

Half Equations Show if Things Have Been Oxidised or Reduced

1) Half equations (see page 37) show how electrons move during a reaction.

2) You could be asked to identify whether something's been oxidised or reduced during a chemical reaction. If you are, looking at half equations is a great way of doing this.

3) Remember, if something loses electrons, then it's been oxidised (and it's a reducing agent). If something gains electrons, then it's been reduced (and it's an oxidising agent).

- Iron atoms are oxidised to Fe^{2+} ions when they react with dilute acid: $Fe + 2H^+ \rightarrow Fe^{2+} + H_2$
- The iron atoms lose electrons. They're oxidised by the hydrogen ions: $Fe \rightarrow Fe^{2+} + 2e^-$
- The hydrogen ions gain electrons. They're reduced by the iron atoms: $2H^+ + 2e^- \rightarrow H_2$

EXAMPLE: Work out which element has been reduced in the following equation: $Cu^{2+} + Mg \rightarrow Cu + Mg^{2+}$

1) Work out whether each element has lost or gained electrons by writing out the half equations.

2) Reduction involves the gain of electrons, so find the element that's gained electrons.

$Cu^{2+} + 2e^- \rightarrow Cu$
$Mg \rightarrow Mg^{2+} + 2e^-$
Add electrons so the charges on each side of the equation balance.

Copper ions have gained two electrons to become copper atoms, so **copper** is reduced.

Electrolysis Involves Oxidation and Reduction

There's more on electrolysis on the next page.

1) Electrolysis is the breaking down of a substance using electricity.

2) An electric current is passed through an electrolyte (a molten or dissolved ionic compound), causing it to decompose.

This creates a flow of charge through the electrolyte.

3) The positive ions (cations) in the electrolyte will move towards the cathode (negative electrode) and are reduced (gain electrons). The negative ions (anions) in the electrolyte will move towards the anode (positive electrode) and are oxidised (lose electrons).

4) As ions gain or lose electrons they form the uncharged substances and are discharged from the solution.

5) An electrochemical cell is a circuit, made up of the anode, cathode, electrolyte, a power source and the wires that connect the two electrodes.

Put your feet up... inhale... exhale... and redox...

It might seem pretty useless now, but if electrolysis comes up in the exam, you'll want to know it...

Q1 Identify the oxidising agent in this reaction: $Zn + 2H^+ \rightarrow Zn^{2+} + H_2$ [1 mark]

Q2 In electrolysis, which ions are attracted towards the cathode? [1 mark]

Electrolysis

This stuff is electrifying. You'll be on the edge of your seat with all this fun, fun, fun <u>electrolysis</u>.

In Molten Ionic Solids, There's Only One Source of Ions

1) An <u>ionic solid can't</u> be electrolysed because the ions are in fixed positions and <u>can't move</u>.
2) <u>Molten ionic compounds</u> can be electrolysed because the ions can <u>move freely</u> and conduct electricity.
3) Positive <u>metal ions</u> are <u>reduced</u> (i.e. they <u>gain</u> electrons) to <u>atoms</u> at the cathode.
4) Negative <u>ions</u> are <u>oxidised</u> (i.e. they <u>lose electrons</u>) to atoms at the <u>anode</u>.
5) In the example of $PbBr_2$, you'd see a <u>brown vapour</u> of bromine gas at the anode. Beads of <u>molten lead</u> would form at the cathode.

$$Pb^{2+} + 2e^- \rightarrow Pb$$ $$2Br^- \rightarrow Br_2 + 2e^-$$

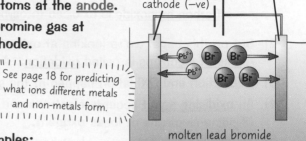

See page 18 for predicting what ions different metals and non-metals form.

molten lead bromide

6) It's easy to predict what products you get when you electrolyse <u>molten</u> substances — it's getting the <u>half equations</u> right that's tougher. Here are some examples:

Molten Electrolyte	Product at Cathode	Half equation at Cathode	Product at Anode	Half equation at Anode
lead iodide, PbI_2	lead	$Pb^{2+} + 2e^- \rightarrow Pb$	iodine	$2I^- \rightarrow I_2 + 2e^-$
potassium chloride, KCl	potassium	$K^+ + e^- \rightarrow K$	chlorine	$2Cl^- \rightarrow Cl_2 + 2e^-$
aluminium oxide, Al_2O_3	aluminium	$Al^{3+} + 3e^- \rightarrow Al$	oxygen	$2O^{2-} \rightarrow O_2 + 4e^-$

Electrolysis of Aqueous Solutions is a Bit More Complicated

1) In <u>aqueous solutions</u>, as well as the <u>ions</u> from the ionic compound, there will be <u>hydrogen ions</u> (H^+) and <u>hydroxide ions</u> (OH^-) from the <u>water</u>: $H_2O_{(l)} \rightleftharpoons H^+_{(aq)} + OH^-_{(aq)}$

2) At the <u>cathode</u>, if H^+ ions and metal ions are present, <u>hydrogen gas</u> will be produced if the metal is <u>more reactive</u> than hydrogen (e.g. sodium). If the metal is <u>less reactive</u> than hydrogen (e.g. copper or silver), then a solid layer of the <u>pure metal</u> will be produced instead.

Some reactivity series (see page 57) include hydrogen in the list. You can use these to find out which metals are more or less reactive than hydrogen.

3) At the <u>anode</u>, if <u>halide ions</u> (Cl^-, Br^-, I^-) are present, molecules of chlorine, bromine or iodine will be formed. If <u>no halide ions</u> are present, then <u>oxygen</u> will be formed from the hydroxide ions.

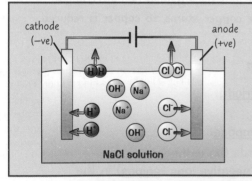

NaCl solution

A solution of <u>sodium chloride</u> ($NaCl$) contains <u>four different ions</u>: Na^+, Cl^-, OH^- and H^+.

- <u>Sodium</u> metal is more reactive than hydrogen. So at the cathode, <u>hydrogen gas</u> is produced.
$$2H^+ + 2e^- \rightarrow H_2$$

- <u>Chloride ions</u> are present in the solution. So at the anode <u>chlorine gas</u> is produced.
$$2Cl^- \rightarrow Cl_2 + 2e^-$$

For more on tests for gases, turn to page 58.

Chlorine and hydrogen gas are released in the example above. You can test for these in the lab:

- Chlorine <u>bleaches</u> damp <u>litmus paper</u>, turning it white. (It may turn <u>red</u> for a moment first though — that's because a solution of chlorine is <u>acidic</u>.)
- Hydrogen makes a "<u>squeaky pop</u>" when burnt with a <u>lighted splint</u>.

Faster shopping at the supermarket — use Electrolleys...

So it's kinda confusing this electrolysis malarkey — you need to take it slow and make sure you get it.

Q1   An aqueous solution of copper bromide, $CuBr_2$, is electrolysed using inert electrodes. Give the half equation to show the reaction occurring at the anode.

[1 mark]

Electrolysis of Copper Sulfate

You may be yawning now, but electrolysis is a really important step in purifying copper.

Here's How to Set Up an Electrochemical Cell

You'll probably have to do an experiment using electrolysis in the lab, so you need to know how to set up an electrochemical cell. Here's how you'd set up a copper sulfate cell:

1) Get two electrodes (you should use inert electrodes, e.g. platinum or carbon). Clean the surfaces of the electrodes using a piece of emery paper (or sandpaper).

2) From this point on, be careful not to touch the surfaces of the metals with your hands — you could transfer grease back onto the strips.

3) Place both electrodes into a beaker filled with your electrolyte.

4) Connect the electrodes to a power supply using crocodile clips and wires.

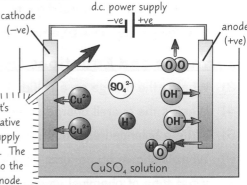

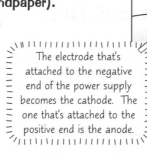

The electrode that's attached to the negative end of the power supply becomes the cathode. The one that's attached to the positive end is the anode.

A solution of copper sulfate ($CuSO_4$) contains four different ions: Cu^{2+}, SO_4^{2-}, H^+ and OH^-.

- Copper metal is less reactive than hydrogen. So at the cathode, copper metal is produced. You'd see a coating of copper forming on the cathode.

$$Cu^{2+} + 2e^- \rightarrow Cu$$

- There aren't any halide ions present. So at the anode, oxygen and water are produced. You'd see bubbles of oxygen gas forming.

$$4OH^- \rightarrow O_2 + 2H_2O + 4e^-$$

Oxygen relights a glowing splint.

Non-Inert Electrodes Take Part in Electrolysis Reactions

1) Non-inert electrodes can decompose into the electrolyte.

2) For example, you could use copper electrodes in a solution of copper sulfate.

3) To set up this electrochemical cell, you should use the same method as the one above, but use copper electrodes, rather than inert carbon or platinum electrodes.

4) As the reaction continues, the mass of the anode will decrease and the mass of the cathode will increase. This is because copper is transferred from the anode to the cathode.

5) The reaction takes a bit of time to happen, you'll need to leave the cell running for 30 minutes or so to get a decent change in mass.

6) If you want to measure how the mass of your electrodes has changed during an experiment like this one, you should dry the electrodes before weighing them — any copper sulfate solution on the electrodes may mean they appear to have a higher mass than they really do...

This is used in the purification of copper by electrolysis (see page 77).

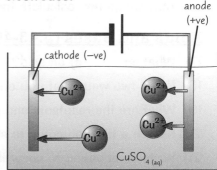

The electrical supply acts by:

- Pulling electrons off copper atoms at the anode, causing them to go into solution as Cu^{2+} ions.

$$\text{Anode: } Cu_{(s)} \rightarrow Cu^{2+}_{(aq)} + 2e^-$$

- Then offering electrons at the cathode to nearby Cu^{2+} ions to turn them back into copper atoms.

$$\text{Cathode: } Cu^{2+}_{(aq)} + 2e^- \rightarrow Cu_{(s)}$$

Electro-lite — low-fat and packed full of important ions...

Phew, made it. Time to celebrate making it to the end of another topic with a question. Hozzah.

Q1   June connects an electrochemical cell, consisting of two copper electrodes and a copper sulfate solution electrolyte, to a power supply and leaves it for 30 minutes. How would you expect the mass of the anode to change during the experiment? Explain your answer.   [2 marks]

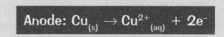
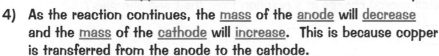

Revision Questions for Topic C3

Well, wasn't that enjoyable? Topic C3 has been my favourite topic so far I think.

- Try these questions and tick off each one when you get it right.
- When you've done all the questions under a heading and are completely happy with it, tick it off.

Conservation of Mass (p.34) ☑

1) In a reaction, how does the mass of products compare with the mass of reactants?

2) Why might the mass of a reaction that occurs in an open vessel appear to decrease?

Formulas and Equations (p.35-37) ☑

3) What is the charge on a sulfide ion?

4) What is the overall charge on an ionic compound?

5) Write a balanced equation for the reaction of magnesium and oxygen gas to form magnesium oxide.

6) What is shown by an ionic equation?

7) What type of chemical equation would you use to show how electrons are transferred in a reaction?

Moles and Calculations (p.38-40) ☑

8) What does Avogadro's constant represent?

9) Give the formula that links the number of moles with mass and relative formula mass.

10) What is meant by a limiting reactant?

11) How can you find the limiting reactant from a balanced equation and the masses of reactants present?

Energy Changes and Reactions (p.41-42) ☑

12) What is the difference between an endothermic and an exothermic reaction?

13) Sketch a reaction profile for an exothermic reaction.

14) What is meant by the term 'activation energy'?

15) Is energy released when bonds are broken or when they are made?

16) How would you calculate the overall energy change in a reaction from the bond energies?

Acids and Bases (p.43-46) ☑

17) What is: a) an acid?   b) a base?   c) an alkali?

18) Name two ways that you could measure the pH of a solution.

19) What are the reactants and products of a neutralisation reaction?

20) Sketch a titration curve to show how the pH of a solution of acid changes as a base is added.

21) Write an equation to show the ionisation of ethanoic acid (CH_3COOH), a weak acid, in solution.

22) Write a balanced equation for the reaction of hydrochloric acid with aluminium.

23) Write a balanced equation to show how copper chloride ($CuCl_2$)
    is made from copper oxide (CuO) and hydrochloric acid.

24) Outline how you could make lead chloride ($PbCl_2$) using a precipitation reaction.

Redox and Electrolysis (p.47-49) ☑

25) Give the two definitions of: a) oxidation,   b) reduction.

26) What is electrolysis?

27) When a molten ionic compound decomposes during electrolysis, at which electrode does the metal form?

28) Outline how you would set up an electrochemical cell using copper sulfate solution and inert electrodes.

29) Why do the masses of non-inert electrodes change during electrolysis?

Group 1 — Alkali Metals

You can predict how different elements will <u>react</u> by looking at where they are in the <u>periodic table</u> — elements in the <u>same group</u> will react in <u>similar ways</u>. Time to take a look at some of the groups, starting with <u>Group 1</u>...

Group 1 Metals are Known as the 'Alkali Metals'

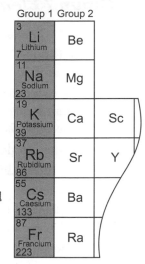

The Group 1 metals are lithium, sodium, potassium, rubidium, caesium and francium.

1) The alkali metals all have <u>one outer electron</u>
— so they have <u>similar chemical properties</u>.

2) They all have the following <u>physical properties</u>:
- <u>Low melting points</u> and <u>boiling points</u> (compared with other metals).
- <u>Low density</u> — lithium, sodium and potassium float on water.
- <u>Very soft</u> — they can be cut with a knife.

3) The alkali metals form <u>ionic</u> compounds. They lose their one outer electron <u>so easily</u> that sharing it would be out of the question, so they <u>don't</u> form covalent bonds.

4) You can test for the presence of Group 1 metal ions using <u>flame tests</u> — see page 60 for more.

Group 1 Metals are Very Reactive

1) The Group 1 metals readily <u>lose</u> their single <u>outer electron</u> to form a <u>1+ ion</u> with a <u>stable electronic structure</u>.

2) The <u>more readily</u> a metal loses its outer electrons, the <u>more reactive</u> it is — so the Group 1 metals are very reactive.

3) As you go <u>down</u> Group 1, the alkali metals get <u>more reactive</u>. The <u>outer electron</u> is more easily <u>lost</u> because it's further from the nucleus (the <u>atomic radius</u> is <u>larger</u>) — so it's less strongly attracted to the nucleus and <u>less energy</u> is needed to remove it.

Reaction with Cold Water Produces a Hydroxide and Hydrogen Gas

1) When the <u>alkali metals</u> are put in <u>water</u>, they react <u>vigorously</u>.

2) The reaction produces <u>hydrogen gas</u> and a <u>hydroxide</u> of the metal (an <u>alkali</u> see page 43). For example, here's the overall equation for the reaction of <u>sodium</u> with <u>water</u>:

Squeaky pop!

A squeaky pop shows H_2 gas is present — see p.58 for more.

$$2Na + 2H_2O \rightarrow 2NaOH + H_2$$
sodium + water → sodium hydroxide + hydrogen

The same reaction happens with all of the alkali metals — make sure you can write balanced equations for them all.

3) The reactivity of Group 1 metals with water (and dilute acid — see below) increases down the group.
- <u>Lithium</u> will <u>move</u> around the surface, <u>fizzing</u> furiously.
- <u>Sodium</u> and <u>potassium</u> do the same, but they also <u>melt</u> in the heat of the reaction. The potassium even gets hot enough to <u>ignite</u> the hydrogen gas being produced.
- <u>Rubidium</u> and <u>caesium</u> react <u>violently</u> with water, and tend to <u>explode</u> when they get wet...

The alkali metals also react with <u>dilute acids</u>, but with an <u>acid</u> the products are a <u>salt</u> and hydrogen gas.
For example: $2Na + 2HCl \rightarrow 2NaCl + H_2$
sodium + hydrochloric acid → sodium chloride + hydrogen

These reactions are <u>more violent</u> than the ones with water — they can be <u>dangerous</u> to do in a school lab.

And that's why you don't get caesium teaspoons... Amongst other reasons...

Alkali metals are super reactive. In fact they have to be stored in oil — otherwise they just react with the air.

Q1 Explain why the alkali metals become more reactive as you move down Group 1. [3 marks]

Q2 Write a balanced symbol equation for the reaction between lithium (Li) and water. [2 marks]

Group 7 — Halogens

Here's a page on another periodic table group that you need to be familiar with — <u>the halogens</u>.

Group 7 Elements are Known as the Halogens

Group 7 is made up of the elements fluorine, chlorine, bromine, iodine and astatine.

1) All Group 7 elements have <u>7 electrons in their outer shell</u> — so they all have <u>similar chemical properties</u>.

2) The halogens exist as <u>diatomic molecules</u> (e.g. Cl_2, Br_2, I_2). Sharing one pair of electrons in a <u>covalent bond</u> (see page 20) gives both atoms a <u>full outer shell</u>.

3) As you go <u>down Group 7</u>, the <u>melting points</u> and <u>boiling points</u> of the halogens <u>increase</u>.

4) This means that at <u>room temperature</u>:
   - <u>Chlorine</u> (Cl_2) is a fairly reactive, poisonous, <u>green gas</u> (it has a low boiling point).
   - <u>Bromine</u> (Br_2) is a poisonous, <u>red-brown liquid</u>, which gives off an <u>orange vapour</u> at room temperature.
   - <u>Iodine</u> (I_2) is a <u>dark grey crystalline solid</u> which gives off a <u>purple vapour</u> when heated.

	Group 6	Group 7	Group 0
			He
	O	9 F Fluorine 19	Ne
	S	17 Cl Chlorine 35.5	Ar
	Se	35 Br Bromine 80	Kr
		53 I Iodine 127	Xe
		85 At Astatine 210	Rn

Reactivity Decreases Going Down Group 7

1) A halogen atom only needs to <u>gain one electron</u> to form a <u>1– ion</u> with a <u>stable electronic structure</u>.

2) The <u>easier</u> it is for a halogen atom to <u>attract</u> an electron, the <u>more reactive</u> the halogen will be.

3) As you go <u>DOWN</u> Group 7, the halogens become <u>less reactive</u> — it gets <u>harder</u> to attract the <u>extra electron</u> to fill the outer shell when it's <u>further away</u> from the nucleus (the <u>atomic radius</u> is <u>larger</u>).

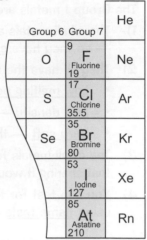

$$Cl + e^- \rightarrow Cl^-$$

The Halogens React With Alkali Metals to Form Salts

The halogens will react vigorously with alkali metals (Group 1 elements, see page 51) to form <u>salts</u> called '<u>metal halides</u>'. For example:

$$2Na + Cl_2 \rightarrow 2NaCl$$
Sodium + Chlorine → Sodium chloride

$$2K + Br_2 \rightarrow 2KBr$$
Potassium + Bromine → Potassium bromide

All the reactions between Group 1 and Group 7 elements follow this pattern — make sure you can write equations for any of them.

The Halogens Undergo Displacement Reactions

1) A <u>more reactive</u> halogen can <u>displace</u> a <u>less reactive</u> one from a salt solution.

2) There's loads more about these reactions coming up on the next page...

Halogens — one electron short of a full shell...

Another page, another periodic table group to learn the properties and the trends of. When you're pretty confident that you've got all the stuff from this page in your head, have a go at the questions below, just to check.

Q1   The melting point of chlorine (Cl_2) is –101.5 °C. Predict whether bromine (Br_2) would be a solid, a liquid or a gas at –101.5 °C. Explain your answer.   [2 marks]

Q2   Write a balanced symbol equation for the reaction between sodium metal (Na) and iodine (I_2).   [2 marks]

Halogen Displacement Reactions

The halogens are a pretty competitive lot really. In fact the <u>more reactive</u> ones will push the <u>less reactive</u> ones out of a compound. How uncivilized — has nobody ever taught them that it's bad manners to push?

A More Reactive Halogen Will Displace a Less Reactive One

1) The elements in Group 7 take part in <u>displacement reactions</u>.

2) A <u>displacement reaction</u> is where a <u>more reactive</u> element 'pushes out' (displaces) a <u>less reactive</u> element from a compound.

3) For example, <u>chlorine</u> is more reactive than <u>bromine</u> (it's higher up Group 7). If you add <u>chlorine water</u> (an <u>aqueous solution</u> of Cl_2) to <u>potassium bromide</u> solution, the chlorine will <u>displace</u> the <u>bromine</u> from the salt solution.

4) The <u>chlorine</u> is reduced to <u>chloride ions</u>, so the salt solution becomes <u>potassium chloride</u>. The <u>bromide ions</u> are oxidised to <u>bromine</u>, which turns the solution <u>orange</u>.

chlorine water

colourless solution — potassium bromide

orange solution — bromine forming in solution

5) The <u>equation</u> for this reaction is shown below:

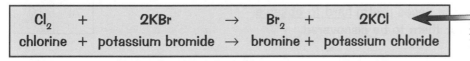

$$Cl_2 + 2KBr \rightarrow Br_2 + 2KCl$$
$$\text{chlorine} + \text{potassium bromide} \rightarrow \text{bromine} + \text{potassium chloride}$$

If you ever need to write an equation for a different halogen displacement reaction, they all follow this pattern.

Displacement Reactions Show Reactivity Trends

PRACTICAL

You can use <u>displacement reactions</u> to show the reactivity trend of the halogens.

1) Start by measuring out a small amount of a <u>halide salt solution</u> in a test tube.

2) Add a few drops of a <u>halogen solution</u> to it and shake the tube gently.

3) If you see a <u>colour change</u>, then a reaction has happened — the halogen has displaced the halide ions from the salt. If no reaction happens, there <u>won't</u> be a colour change.

You should wear a lab coat and goggles when doing this experiment — some of the chemicals are harmful.

4) Repeat the process using different combinations of halide salt and halogen.

5) The table below shows what should happen when you mix different combinations of <u>chlorine</u>, <u>bromine</u> and <u>iodine</u> water with solutions of the salts <u>potassium chloride</u>, <u>potassium bromide</u> and <u>potassium iodide</u>.

Start with:	Potassium chloride solution $KCl_{(aq)}$ — colourless	Potassium bromide solution $KBr_{(aq)}$ — colourless	Potassium iodide solution $KI_{(aq)}$ — colourless
Add chlorine water $Cl_{2\,(aq)}$ — colourless	no reaction	orange solution (Br_2) formed	brown solution (I_2) formed
Add bromine water $Br_{2\,(aq)}$ — orange	no reaction	no reaction	brown solution (I_2) formed
Add iodine water $I_{2\,(aq)}$ — brown	no reaction	no reaction	no reaction

6) <u>Chlorine</u> displaces both bromine and iodine from salt solutions. <u>Bromine</u> can't displace chlorine, but it does displace iodine. <u>Iodine</u> can't displace chlorine or bromine.

7) This shows the <u>reactivity trend</u> — the halogens get <u>less reactive</u> as you go <u>down</u> the group. *This is to do with how easily they gain electrons — see p.52 for more.*

New information displaces old information from my brain...

If you remember that the halogens get less reactive as you go down the group, you can work out what will happen when you mix any halogen with any halide salt. You need to know the colour changes that go with the reactions too.

Q1 A student added a few drops of a halogen solution to some potassium iodide solution. The solution turned brown. She added a few drops of the same halogen solution to some potassium bromide solution. No reaction occurred. Name the halogen solution that the student used. [1 mark]

Topic C4 — Predicting and Identifying Reactions and Products

Group 0 — Noble Gases

The elements in Group 0 of the periodic table are known as the <u>noble gases</u>. 'Noble' here is just being used in the old chemistry sense of being <u>unreactive</u> — nothing to do with them being particularly honourable or good.

Group 0 Elements are All Inert, Colourless Gases

Group 0 elements are called the <u>noble gases</u>. Group 0 is made up of the elements helium, neon, argon, krypton, xenon and radon.

1) All of the elements in Group 0 are <u>colourless gases</u> at room temperature.

2) The noble gases are all <u>monatomic</u> — that just means that their gases are made up of <u>single atoms</u> (not molecules).

3) They're also more or less <u>inert</u> — this means they <u>don't react</u> with much at all. The reason for this is that they have a <u>full outer shell</u> of electrons. This means they <u>don't</u> easily either <u>give up</u> or <u>gain</u> electrons.

4) As the noble gases are inert, they're <u>non-flammable</u> — they won't set on fire.

5) These properties make the gases pretty <u>hard to observe</u> — it took a long time for them to be discovered.

Group 6	Group 7	Group 0
		2 He Helium
O	F	10 Ne Neon 20
S	Cl	18 Ar Argon 40
	Br	36 Kr Krypton 84
I		54 Xe Xenon 131
At		86 Rn Radon 222

There are Patterns in the Properties of the Noble Gases

1) As with the other groups in the periodic table, there are <u>trends</u> in the <u>properties</u> of the noble gases.

2) For example, <u>boiling point</u>, <u>melting point</u> and <u>density</u> all <u>increase</u> as you go <u>down</u> Group 0.

3) You could be given information about a particular <u>property</u> of the noble gases (or Group 1 and Group 7 elements) and asked to use it to <u>estimate the value</u> of this property for a certain element. For example:

EXAMPLE: Use the densities of helium (0.2 kg/m³) and argon (1.8 kg/m³) to predict the density of neon.

Neon comes between helium and argon in the group, so you can predict that its density will be roughly halfway between their densities: (0.2 + 1.8) ÷ 2 = 2.0 ÷ 2 = 1.0

Neon should have a density of about 1.0 kg/m³.

There are other methods you could use for these questions, but don't worry — you'd get marks for any sensible answer.

EXAMPLE: The table on the right shows the melting points of the first five noble gases. Predict the melting point of radon.

Melting points increase as you go down the group, so radon's melting point must be higher than xenon's. To predict how much higher, look at the gaps between the melting points of the other elements:

He to Ne: (−249) − (−272) = 23 Ne to Ar (−189) − (−249) = 60
Ar to Kr: (−157) − (−189) = 32 Kr to Xe: (−112) − (−157) = 45

The gaps aren't exactly the same, so find the average gap: (23 + 60 + 32 + 45) ÷ 4 = 160 ÷ 4 = 40 °C
Now you can just add this average gap to the melting point of xenon.

Radon should have a melting point of about (−112) + 40 = −72 °C.

Element	Melting point (°C)
He	−272
Ne	−249
Ar	−189
Kr	−157
Xe	−112

4) You could be asked about how an element <u>reacts</u> too, so remember — elements in the <u>same group</u> react in <u>similar ways</u> as they all have the same number of <u>electrons</u> in their <u>outer shells</u>. And, all you need to do to find which group an element is in is look at the <u>periodic table</u>. Simple.

What's a pirate's favourite element? Arrrrgon...

The noble gases might seem a bit dull, given how unreactive they are, but they're not so bad. They'd be pretty good at hide and seek for a start. And what would helium balloon sellers be without them? Deflated — that's what.

Q1 The boiling points of the first four noble gases are: helium = −269 °C, neon = −246 °C, argon = −186 °C and krypton = −153 °C. Predict the boiling point of xenon. [1 mark]

Transition Metals

You'll find the transition metals sitting together slap bang in the middle of the periodic table. They've got plenty of different properties that you need to know about — so grab a cup of tea and a biscuit, and read on...

The Transition Metals Sit in the Middle of the Periodic Table

A lot of everyday metals are transition metals (e.g. copper, iron, zinc, gold, silver, platinum) — but there are loads of others as well.

If you get asked about a transition metal you've never heard of — don't panic. These 'new' transition metals will follow all the properties you've already learnt for the others.

These are the transition metals

Sc	Ti	V	Cr	Mn	Fe	Co	Ni	Cu	Zn
Y	Zr	Nb	Mo	Tc	Ru	Rh	Pd	Ag	Cd
La	Hf	Ta	W	Re	Os	Ir	Pt	Au	Hg
Ac	Rf	Db	Sg	Bh	Hs	Mt	Ds	Rg	Cn

Transition Metals Have Typical Metallic Properties

1) The transition metals have all the typical properties of metals (see page 24) — they are hard, strong and shiny materials that conduct heat and electricity well.

2) They have high melting points (with the exception of mercury, which is liquid at room temperature).

3) They also have high densities. For example, at room temperature, potassium (a Group 1 metal) has a density of 0.9 g/cm^3, while copper has a density of 9.0 g/cm^3, and iron has a density of 7.9 g/cm^3.

Transition Metals and Their Compounds Make Good Catalysts

1) Iron is the catalyst used in the Haber process for making ammonia (see p.80).

2) Vanadium pentoxide (V_2O_5) is the catalyst for making sulfuric acid in the Contact Process (see p.82).

Transition Metals Often Have More Than One Ion, e.g. Fe²⁺, Fe³⁺

Two other examples are copper, which has Cu^+ and Cu^{2+} ions, and chromium which has Cr^{2+} and Cr^{3+} ions.

Their Compounds are Very Colourful

The compounds of transition elements are colourful. What colour they are depends on what transition metal ion they contain — e.g. compounds containing Fe^{2+} ions are usually light green, ones with Fe^{3+} ions are orange/brown (e.g. rust, see page 79) and those with Cu^{2+} ions are often blue.

Not bothered...

Transition Metals are Relatively Unreactive

1) Transition metals are much less reactive than Group 1 and Group 2 metals.

2) For example, most transition metals will react with dilute acids to form metal salts (see next page), but these reactions happen much more slowly than the reaction of metals like sodium and magnesium with dilute acids.

You can't get much more colourful than transition metal ions...

Transition metals are everywhere. They make good catalysts, iron's used to make steel for construction, copper's so unreactive you can use it to make water pipes, and you can even use their pretty compounds to colour stained glass.

Q1   Name one industrial process that uses a transition metal catalyst. Name the catalyst used.   [1 mark]

Q2   Rubidium is a Group 1 metal. Palladium is a transition metal.
a) Predict which of these two metals will have a higher density. Explain your answer.   [1 mark]
b) Predict which of these two metals will be more reactive. Explain your answer.   [1 mark]

Reactivity of Metals

Reactive metals tend to do exciting, fizzy things when you drop them into acid or water. If you do the same with an unreactive metal, it'll just sit there. How boring. Here's a bit more detail on reactivity experiments...

How Metals React With Acids Tells You About Their Reactivity

1) The easier it is for a metal atom to lose its outer electrons and form a positive ion, the more reactive it will be.

2) Here's a classic experiment that you can do to show that some metals are more reactive than others. All you do is to place little pieces of various metals into dilute hydrochloric acid:

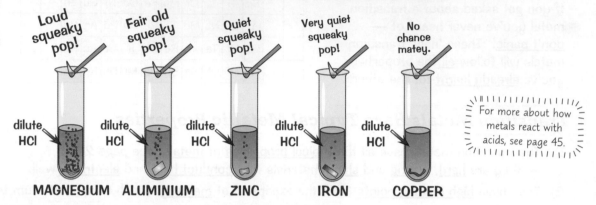

For more about how metals react with acids, see page 45.

3) The more reactive the metal is, the faster the reaction will go.

4) Very reactive metals (e.g. magnesium) will fizz vigorously, less reactive metals (e.g. zinc) will bubble a bit, and unreactive metals (e.g. copper) will not react with dilute acids at all.

5) You can show that hydrogen is forming using the burning splint test (see page 58). The louder the squeaky pop, the more hydrogen has been made in the time period and the more reactive the metal is.

6) The speed of reaction is also indicated by the rate at which the bubbles of hydrogen are given off — the faster the bubbles form, the faster the reaction and the more reactive the metal.

You could also follow the rate of the reaction by using a gas syringe to measure the volume of gas given off at regular time intervals.

Metals Also React With Water

The reactions of metals with water also show the reactivity of metals. This is the basic reaction:

> metal + water → metal hydroxide + hydrogen
> (Or: less reactive metal + steam → metal oxide + hydrogen)

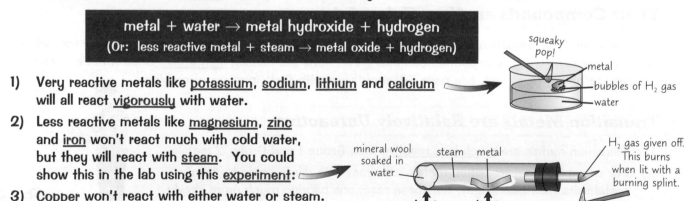

1) Very reactive metals like potassium, sodium, lithium and calcium will all react vigorously with water.

2) Less reactive metals like magnesium, zinc and iron won't react much with cold water, but they will react with steam. You could show this in the lab using this experiment:

3) Copper won't react with either water or steam.

I AM NOT HIGHLY REACTIVE — OK...

This stuff isn't too bad — who knows, you might even get to have a go at these experiments in class...

Q1 A student is given small samples of three metals, A, B and C. He places them in dilute hydrochloric acid. Nothing happens to Metal A. Metal B fizzes vigorously. The gas given off gives a loud squeaky pop when lit with a burning splint. Metal C fizzes a bit and the gas given off gives a quiet squeaky pop when lit.
    a) Put the three metals in order, from most reactive to least reactive. [1 mark]
    b) One of the metals was zinc, one was magnesium, and one was copper. Use this information to identify metals A, B and C. [1 mark]

The Reactivity Series and Displacement

On the previous page, you covered some reactions that help you work out how <u>reactive</u> a <u>metal</u> is. You can use information like this to put the metals in order of their <u>reactivity</u>. Which is more useful than it sounds, promise.

The Reactivity Series Shows How Reactive Metals Are

A <u>reactivity series</u> is just a table that lists <u>metals</u> in order of their <u>reactivity</u>. Here's an example:

The Reactivity Series	
Potassium	K
Sodium	Na
Calcium	Ca
Magnesium	Mg
Aluminium	Al
Zinc	Zn
Iron	Fe
Copper	Cu
Silver	Ag

most reactive

least reactive

The reactivity series can help you to work out the best method of extracting a metal from its ore — see page 76 for more.

I shall not react.

More Reactive Metals Displace Less Reactive Ones

1) If you put a <u>more reactive metal</u> into a solution of a <u>less reactive metal salt</u>, the reactive metal will <u>replace</u> the <u>less reactive metal</u> in the salt.

> <u>Example</u>: if you put an <u>iron nail</u> in a solution of <u>copper sulfate</u>, the more reactive iron will "<u>kick out</u>" the less reactive copper from the salt. You end up with <u>iron sulfate solution</u> and <u>copper metal</u>.
>
> copper sulfate + iron → iron sulfate + copper
> $$CuSO_4 + Fe → FeSO_4 + Cu$$

2) If you put a <u>less reactive metal</u> into a solution of a <u>more reactive metal salt</u>, <u>nothing</u> will happen.

> <u>Example</u>: if you put a small piece of silver metal into a solution of <u>copper sulfate</u>, nothing will happen. The more reactive metal (copper) is already in the salt.

3) You can use displacement reactions to <u>work out</u> where in the reactivity series a metal should go.

> <u>Example</u>: A student adds some <u>metals</u> to <u>metal salt solutions</u> and records whether any <u>reactions</u> happen. Use her table of results, below, to work out an <u>order of reactivity</u> for the metals.
>
> | | copper nitrate | magnesium chloride | zinc sulfate |
> |---|---|---|---|
> | copper | no reaction | no reaction | no reaction |
> | magnesium | magnesium nitrate and copper formed | no reaction | magnesium sulfate and zinc formed |
> | zinc | zinc nitrate and copper formed | no reaction | no reaction |
>
> • Magnesium <u>displaces</u> both <u>copper</u> and <u>zinc</u>, so it must be <u>more reactive</u> than both.
> • Copper <u>is displaced by</u> both <u>magnesium</u> and <u>zinc</u>, so it must be <u>less reactive</u> than both.
> • Zinc <u>can displace copper</u>, but <u>not magnesium</u>, so it must go between them.
> The <u>order of reactivity</u>, <u>from most to least</u>, is:
> <u>magnesium</u>, <u>zinc</u>, <u>copper</u>

And that's why Iron Man never goes swimming in copper sulfate...

You could be given the results of an experiment and have to use them to put the metals into an order of reactivity, or you could be told their reactivities and then asked to predict how they'll react — make sure you can do both.

Q1   State whether magnesium would displace iron from iron sulfate solution. Explain your answer.   [1 mark]

Q2   Tin sits between iron and copper in the reactivity series.
State whether tin would displace zinc from zinc sulfate solution and explain your answer.   [1 mark]

Tests for Gases

There are lots of ways of <u>testing</u> for different <u>gases</u> — some of them involve bubbling the gas through a liquid, some involve testing it with litmus paper, and some involve trying to set fire to it. Doesn't sound dangerous at all...

Testing for Gases Can be Dangerous

1) When you're testing for a mystery gas, you need to be <u>careful</u>. Some gases are pretty <u>nasty</u>, so you don't want to just go spewing them out into your classroom.

2) So, you should carry out all of the following tests in a <u>fume cupboard</u>, that way there's not as much of a risk that you, or your classmates, will go inhaling a <u>toxic gas</u>.

Test for Carbon Dioxide Using Limewater

1) You can test to see if a gas is <u>carbon dioxide</u> by bubbling it through <u>limewater</u>.

2) If the gas is carbon dioxide, the limewater will <u>turn cloudy</u>.

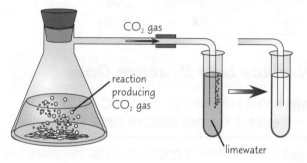

Test for Hydrogen Using a Lighted Splint

1) Hydrogen makes a '<u>squeaky pop</u>' with a <u>lighted splint</u>.

2) The noise comes from the hydrogen burning with the oxygen in the air to form water.

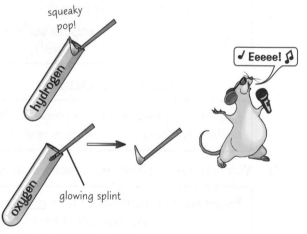

Test for Oxygen Using a Glowing Splint

You can <u>test</u> for oxygen by checking if the gas will <u>relight</u> a <u>glowing splint</u>.

Test for Chlorine Using Damp Blue Litmus Paper

1) You can test to see if a gas is <u>chlorine</u> by holding a piece of <u>damp blue litmus paper</u> over it.

2) If the gas is chlorine, it will <u>bleach</u> the litmus paper, turning it <u>white</u>.

3) It may also turn <u>red</u> for a moment first — that's because a solution of chlorine is <u>acidic</u> (see page 43 for more on acids).

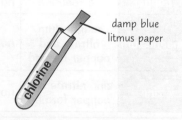

Bleach, cloudy and squeaky pop — the world's worst cereal mascots.

I'm afraid this is just one of those pages where the only thing to do is sit down and learn all four of these gas tests, including what a positive result would be, until they're properly lodged in your memory. Then try the questions...

Q1 Describe how you could test a gas to see if it was oxygen. State what a positive result would be. [2 marks]

Q2 A student performs tests on two gases, gas A and gas B. Gas A bleaches damp blue litmus paper. Gas B ignites with a squeaky pop when tested with a lighted splint. Identify the two gases. [2 marks]

Tests for Anions

Have you ever wondered how you could identify a mystery anion (negative ion) in a solution? If so, then this is definitely the page for you. If not, then tough luck, you're going to need to know it anyway.

Test for Halide Ions Using Silver Nitrate Solution

To test for chloride ions (Cl⁻), bromide ions (Br⁻) or iodide ions (I⁻), add some dilute nitric acid (HNO₃), followed by a few drops of silver nitrate solution (AgNO₃).

The nitric acid is added first to get rid of any carbonate ions — they produce a pale precipitate with silver nitrate too, which would confuse the results. You can't use hydrochloric acid, because you'd be adding chloride ions.

A chloride gives a **white** precipitate of silver chloride.

$$Ag^+_{(aq)} + Cl^-_{(aq)} \longrightarrow AgCl_{(s)}$$

A bromide gives a **cream** precipitate of silver bromide.

$$Ag^+_{(aq)} + Br^-_{(aq)} \longrightarrow AgBr_{(s)}$$

An iodide gives a **yellow** precipitate of silver iodide.

$$Ag^+_{(aq)} + I^-_{(aq)} \longrightarrow AgI_{(s)}$$

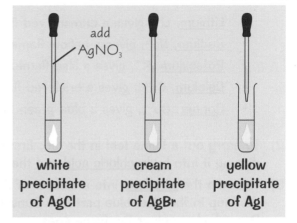

add AgNO₃

white precipitate of AgCl

cream precipitate of AgBr

yellow precipitate of AgI

Test for Carbonates Using Hydrochloric Acid

1) To test for carbonate ions in solution, first add some barium chloride solution.
   If there are carbonate ions present, this will produce a white precipitate of barium carbonate.

2) Then you add some dilute hydrochloric acid.

3) If there are carbonate ions present, the mixture will fizz — this is because the carbonate will react with the acid to produce carbon dioxide gas:

$$\text{barium carbonate} + \text{acid} \rightarrow \text{barium ions} + \text{carbon dioxide} + \text{water}$$
$$BaCO_{3(s)} + 2H^+_{(aq)} \rightarrow Ba^{2+}_{(aq)} + CO_{2(g)} + H_2O_{(l)}$$

4) If you collect the gas and pass it through limewater, the limewater should turn cloudy (see last page).

5) Once all of the barium carbonate has reacted, you'll end up with a colourless solution containing Ba²⁺ ions.

Test for Sulfate Ions Using Barium Chloride Solution

1) The test for sulfate ions in solution is similar to the test for carbonate ions.

2) First you add some barium chloride solution.
   If there are sulfate ions in the solution, a white precipitate, of barium sulfate will form:

$$\text{barium ions} + \text{sulfate ions} \rightarrow \text{barium sulfate}$$
$$Ba^{2+}_{(aq)} + SO_4^{2-}_{(aq)} \rightarrow BaSO_{4(s)}$$

3) Then you add some dilute hydrochloric acid to the test sample.

4) Barium sulfate will **not** react with dilute hydrochloric acid, so the white precipitate will **not dissolve**.
   (That's how you know you've got sulfate ions and **not** carbonate ions.)

Chop them and see if you cry — oh wait, you said test for anions...

Another three tests to learn here I'm afraid — remember to learn how to do each test as well as what the results show.

Q1   A student adds some dilute nitric acid to a solution, followed by some silver nitrate solution.
      A cream precipitate forms. What does this tell the student about their solution?   [1 mark]

Q2   Describe how you would test a solution to see if it contained sulfate ions.   [4 marks]

Tests for Cations

So now you know how to work out what the anion in a mystery compound is. Time to find out what tests you can do to identify the <u>positive ions</u> (<u>cations</u>) in a compound. Don't say I don't spoil you...

You Can Use Flame Tests to Identify Metal Ions

Compounds of some metals produce a characteristic colour when heated in a flame.

1) You can test for various <u>metal ions</u> by putting your substance in a <u>flame</u> and seeing what <u>colour</u> the flame goes.

- <u>Lithium</u>, Li^+, gives a crimson red flame.
- <u>Sodium</u>, Na^+, gives a yellow flame.
- <u>Potassium</u>, K^+, gives a lilac flame.
- <u>Calcium</u>, Ca^{2+}, gives a brick red flame.
- <u>Copper</u>, Cu^{2+}, gives a blue-green flame.

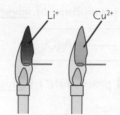

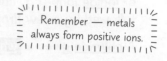
Remember — metals always form positive ions.

2) To carry out a flame test in the lab, first <u>clean</u> a <u>nichrome wire loop</u> by dipping it into <u>hydrochloric acid</u> and then rinsing it in <u>deionised water</u>.

3) Then dip the <u>wire loop</u> into a sample of the <u>metal compound</u> and put the loop in the clear blue part of a Bunsen flame (the hottest bit). Record what <u>colour</u> the flame goes.

This test only works if the mystery compound contains just one type of metal ion — otherwise you'll get a confusing mixture of colours.

Some Metal Ions Form a Coloured Precipitate with Sodium Hydroxide

This is also a test for metal ions, but it's slightly more complicated:

1) Many <u>metal hydroxides</u> are <u>insoluble</u> and precipitate out of solution when formed. Some of these hydroxides have a <u>characteristic colour</u>.

2) For this test, you add a few drops of <u>sodium hydroxide solution</u> to a solution of your mystery compound.

3) If a <u>hydroxide precipitate</u> forms, you can use its <u>colour</u> to tell which metal ion was in the compound.

Metal ion	Colour of precipitate	Ionic equation
Calcium, Ca^{2+}	White	$Ca^{2+}_{(aq)} + 2OH^-_{(aq)} \rightarrow Ca(OH)_{2(s)}$
Copper, Cu^{2+}	Blue	$Cu^{2+}_{(aq)} + 2OH^-_{(aq)} \rightarrow Cu(OH)_{2(s)}$
Iron(II), Fe^{2+}	Green	$Fe^{2+}_{(aq)} + 2OH^-_{(aq)} \rightarrow Fe(OH)_{2(s)}$
Iron(III), Fe^{3+}	Brown	$Fe^{3+}_{(aq)} + 3OH^-_{(aq)} \rightarrow Fe(OH)_{3(s)}$
Zinc, Zn^{2+}	White at first, but then redissolves in excess NaOH to form a colourless solution.	$Zn^{2+}_{(aq)} + 2OH^-_{(aq)} \rightarrow Zn(OH)_{2(s)}$ Then: $Zn(OH)_{2(s)} + 2OH^-_{(aq)} \rightarrow Zn(OH)_4^{2-}_{(aq)}$

There's more about ionic equations and how to write them on page 37.

Nobody presses my shirts better than Mister Furryboots...

If you're having trouble remembering that anions are negative ions and cations are positive, try imagining a happy (positive) cat doing the ironing. It might even make you smile in the middle of an exam, which is definitely a plus.

Q1   In a flame test, if a compound gives a brick red flame, what would this tell you?   [1 mark]

Q2   A student adds a few drops of sodium hydroxide solution to another solution.
A green precipitate forms. What does this tell you about the solution?   [1 mark]

Chemical Analysis

You've just seen loads of tests that you can do <u>by hand</u> in a lab to help you identify gases and ions. Well, you can also get some high tech <u>machines</u> that will analyse mystery substances for you.

You Can Use Machines to Analyse Substances

1) You can analyse and identify elements and compounds using <u>instrumental methods</u> — this just means using <u>machines</u> (rather than a person doing chemical tests manually).

2) Instrumental analysis is used in science research labs, but also in medical labs, police forensics work, environmental analysis and testing products in industry.

3) There are a number of <u>advantages</u> to instrumental methods:

- They are very <u>sensitive</u> — they can detect even the tiniest amounts of a substance.
- They are very <u>fast</u> (and tests can even be automated).
- They are very <u>accurate</u> — they don't involve human error, as manual analysis does.

4) There are lots of different ways that chemists use machines to <u>analyse samples</u> and <u>identify chemicals</u>. Here are some examples:

- <u>INFRARED SPECTROSCOPY</u>: This technique produces a <u>graph</u> showing which <u>frequencies</u> of infrared radiation a molecule will <u>absorb</u> (or <u>transmit</u>). You can use the absorbance pattern on the graph to <u>identify</u> the molecule.

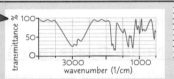

A graph produced by a spectrometer is called a spectrum.

- <u>ULTRAVIOLET (UV) SPECTROSCOPY</u>: Similar to infrared spectroscopy, but using <u>ultraviolet light</u>.
- <u>GAS CHROMATOGRAPHY</u> (see page 30): Used to <u>separate out</u> the chemicals in a mixture. This technique produces a <u>graph</u> (<u>chromatogram</u>) with one peak for each chemical. The <u>time</u> that each chemical takes to pass through the machine (<u>retention time</u>) can be used to <u>identify it</u>.
- <u>MASS SPECTROMETRY</u>: A technique that can be used to find the <u>relative molecular mass</u> of a mystery compound (or the <u>relative atomic mass</u> of a mystery element).

You Can Identify Unknown Substances Using Instrumental Analysis

You could be given the <u>results</u> of an instrumental analysis and asked to <u>interpret</u> them. Here's an example.

EXAMPLE:

A mixture made up of different amounts of three compounds was analysed using gas chromatography. The chromatogram produced by the mixture is shown on the right.

The table below shows the retention times of four pure compounds. Use the data in the table to identify the compound that caused peak C on the chromatogram.

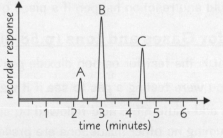

Substance	Retention time (min)
propane	2.25
butane	3
pentane	3.75
hexane	4.5

Peak C (the peak on the right of the chromatogram) has a retention time of 4.5 minutes. The compound in the table with a retention time of 4.5 minutes is hexane.

The compound that caused peak C was hexane.

Unfortunately, you can't get a machine to sit exams for you...

If you are ever given the results of an instrumental test to analyse, as in the example on this page, don't panic — just remember that all the information you need will be right there in the question. And speaking of questions...

Q1   In the example above, which of the substances shown in the table is not in the mixture?   [1 mark]

Revision Questions for Topic C4

Hooray, that's the end of <u>Topic C4</u> — now have a go at these questions to make sure you've really got it.

- Try these questions and <u>tick off each one</u> when you <u>get it right</u>.
- When you've done <u>all the questions</u> under a heading and are <u>completely happy</u> with it, tick it off.

<u>Group 1 — Alkali Metals (p.51)</u> ☑

1) How many electrons does an alkali metal atom have in its outer shell? ☑
2) List three typical properties of the alkali metals. ☑
3) Write a balanced symbol equation to show the reaction between sodium and water. ☑

<u>Group 7 — Halogens (p.52-53)</u> ☑

4) Describe how the reactivity of the elements changes as you go down Group 7. ☑
5) Give the name of the salt formed when potassium reacts with bromine. ☑
6) Chlorine (Cl_2) can displace bromine from potassium bromide (KBr).
   a) Write an equation for this reaction.
   b) Describe the colour change that you would see when this reaction happened. ☑
7) Can iodine displace bromine from potassium bromide solution? ☑

<u>Group 0 — Noble Gases (p.54)</u> ☑

8) True or false? The noble gases generally exist as diatomic molecules. ☑
9) Why are the elements in Group 0 inert? ☑

<u>Transition Metals (p.55)</u> ☑

10) Whereabouts in the periodic table would you find the transition metals? ☑
11) List five typical properties of a transition metal element. ☑

<u>Metals and Reactivity (p.56-57)</u> ☑

12) True or false? The easier it is for a metal atom to form a positive ion, the more reactive it will be. ☑
13) You are given samples of four mystery metals and some dilute hydrochloric acid.
    Briefly describe how you could use these things to work out a reactivity series for the four metals. ☑
14) Magnesium is above zinc in the reactivity series.
    Would any reaction happen if a piece of magnesium metal was put in zinc sulfate solution? ☐

<u>Tests for Gases and Ions (p.58-60)</u> ☑

15) What is the test for carbon dioxide gas? ☑
16) If you were testing a gas to see if it was chlorine, describe what a positive result would look like. ☑
17) You add dilute nitric acid followed by silver nitrate solution to a solution containing chloride ions.
    Assuming no other halide ions are present, describe what you will see. ☑
18) What two reagents do you need to use when testing for sulfate ions? ☑
19) What colour flame does a compound containing potassium ions produce in a flame test? ☑
20) What would you see if you added sodium hydroxide solution to a solution containing Fe^{3+} ions? ☑

<u>Chemical Analysis (p.61)</u> ☑

21) List the three main advantages of using instrumental methods to analyse chemicals. ☑
22) Name two examples of instrumental analysis methods. ☑

Concentration

Concentration is just how much stuff you have in a solution. Brace yourself — it involves some calculations...

Concentration is a Measure of How Crowded Things Are

1 dm³
= 1 litre
= 1000 cm³

1) The more solute (the solid you're dissolving) you dissolve in a given volume, the more crowded the molecules are and the more concentrated the solution.

2) Concentration can be measured in grams per dm³ — so 1 gram of stuff dissolved in 1 dm³ of solution has a concentration of 1 gram per dm³.

3) Here's the formula for finding concentration from the mass of solute:

concentration = mass of solute ÷ volume of solution

mass (g)
concentration (g/dm³)
volume (dm³)

$$\frac{m}{c \times V}$$

EXAMPLE: 25 g of copper sulfate is dissolved in 500 cm³ of water. What's the concentration in g/dm³?

1) Make sure the values are in the right units. The mass is already in g, but you need to convert the volume to dm³.

1000 cm³ = 1 dm³, so
500 cm³ = (500 ÷ 1000) dm³ = 0.5 dm³

2) Now just substitute the values into the formula:

concentration = 25 ÷ 0.5 = **50 g/dm³**

EXAMPLE: What mass of sodium chloride is in 300 cm³ of solution with a concentration of 12 g/dm³?

1) Rearrange the formula so that mass is by itself.

mass = concentration × volume

2) Put the volume into the right units.

300 cm³ = (300 ÷ 1000) dm³ = 0.3 dm³

3) Substitute the values into the rearranged formula.

mass = 12 × 0.3 = **3.6 g**

4) Concentrations are often given in moles per dm³ instead (see next page). To convert from g/dm³ to mol/dm³, you just divide the concentration in g/dm³ by the relative formula mass of the solute.

A Standard Solution Has a Known Concentration

If you're making a standard solution with a concentration in mol/dm³, work out how many moles of solid you need, then convert it to grams.

A standard solution is any solution that you know the concentration of. Making a standard solution needs careful measuring and a hint of maths.

Example: Make 250 cm³ of a 314 g/dm³ solution of sodium chloride.

1) First work out how many grams of solute you need using the formula:
mass = concentration × volume
In this case, it's 314 g/dm³ × 0.25 dm³ = 78.5 g

2) Now weigh out this mass — put an empty beaker on a mass balance and reset it to zero, then add the correct mass.

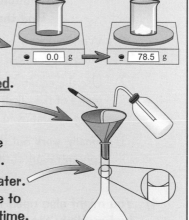

0.0 g   78.5 g

3) Add deionised water to the beaker and stir until all the solute has dissolved.

4) Tip the solution into a volumetric flask — make sure it's the right size for the volume you're making. Use a funnel to make sure it all goes in.

5) Rinse the beaker and stirring rod with deionised water and add that to the flask too. This makes sure there's no solute clinging to the beaker or rod.

6) Top the flask up to the correct volume (250 cm³) with more deionised water. Make sure the bottom of the meniscus is on the line. When you get close to the line, use a dropping pipette to add the last bit of water one drop at a time.

7) Stopper the flask and turn it upside down a few times to mix the solution.

A troop of soldiers standing to attention — it's a mass of salutes...

I know this is chemistry, but unfortunately you have to be able to do a bit of maths too... Best get practising.

Q1   What mass of sodium hydroxide would you need to make up 200 cm³ of a 55 g/dm³ solution?   [2 marks]

Q2   Describe how to make a standard solution of a given volume and concentration (in g/dm³).   [6 marks]

Titrations

Titrations are bad experiments for clumsy people (like me). Lots of big bits of glass, just waiting to be dropped.

Titrations are Used to Find Out Concentrations

PRACTICAL

1) Titrations allow you to find out <u>exactly</u> how much acid is needed to <u>neutralise</u> a given quantity of alkali (or vice versa).

2) Using a <u>pipette</u>, measure out a set volume of the <u>alkali</u> into a flask. Add a few drops of an <u>indicator</u> — usually <u>phenolphthalein</u> or <u>methyl orange</u>.
You can't use Universal indicator — it changes colour gradually and you want a single colour change.

3) Fill a <u>burette</u> with a <u>standard solution</u> (a <u>known concentration</u>) of acid.
Keep the burette below eye level while you fill it — you don't want to be looking up if any acid spills.

4) Use the burette to add the acid to the alkali a bit at a time. <u>Swirl</u> the flask regularly. Go <u>slowly</u> (a drop at a time) when the alkali's almost neutralised.
To work out when this is, do a rough titration first. Don't worry about recording the exact end point first time, just note the approximate amount of acid you need, then go slowly as you get near this amount on the next run.

5) The indicator <u>changes colour</u> when <u>all</u> the alkali has been <u>neutralised</u> (this is called the end point) — phenolphthalein is <u>pink</u> in <u>alkalis</u> but <u>colourless</u> in <u>acids</u>, and methyl orange is <u>yellow</u> in <u>alkalis</u> but <u>red</u> in <u>acids</u>.

6) <u>Record</u> the <u>volume</u> of acid used to <u>neutralise</u> the alkali (called the <u>titre</u>).

7) <u>Repeat</u> this process a few times, making sure you get <u>very similar</u> results each time. You can then take the <u>mean</u> (see page 7) of your results.

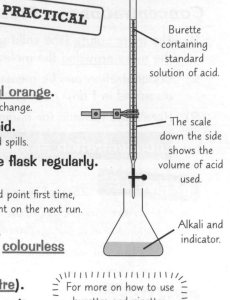
Burette containing standard solution of acid.

The scale down the side shows the volume of acid used.

Alkali and indicator.

For more on how to use burettes and pipettes, see page 102

You Can Calculate the Concentration Using Your Titration Results

1) You saw on the last page that concentration can be measured in g/dm³. The <u>concentration</u> of a solution can also be measured in <u>moles per dm³</u> — so 1 mole of a substance dissolved in 1 dm³ of solution has a concentration of <u>1 mole per dm³</u> (or 1 mol/dm³).

2) The formula for finding <u>concentrations</u> in <u>mol/dm³</u> is similar to the one for g/dm³:

concentration = number of moles ÷ volume of solution

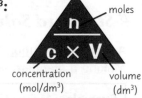
moles
concentration (mol/dm³)
volume (dm³)

3) You can use the results of a <u>titration experiment</u> to calculate the concentration of the alkali when you know the concentration of the acid (or vice versa).

 **EXAMPLE:**

It takes 25.0 cm³ of 0.100 mol/dm³ sulfuric acid to neutralise 30.0 cm³ of sodium hydroxide solution. The equation for this reaction is: $2NaOH + H_2SO_4 \rightarrow Na_2SO_4 + 2H_2O$
Find the concentration of the alkali in mol/dm³.

1) Work out how many <u>moles</u> of acid you have, using the formula: moles = concentration × volume

moles = 0.100 × (25.0 ÷ 1000)
= 0.00250 moles of H_2SO_4

Convert the volume into dm³. (1000 cm³ = 1 dm³)

2) Use the equation to work out how many <u>moles</u> of the alkali you must have had, using the ratios in the balanced equation.

1 mole of H_2SO_4 reacts with 2 moles of NaOH
So 0.00250 moles of H_2SO_4 must react with 0.00250 × 2 = 0.00500 moles of NaOH

3) Finally, work out the <u>concentration</u> of the alkali.

concentration = number of moles ÷ volume
= 0.00500 ÷ (30.0 ÷ 1000) —— Again, convert the volume into dm³.
= 0.1666... mol/dm³ = 0.167 mol/dm³

4) You might also need to convert a concentration in mol/dm³ into g/dm³. To do this, you just multiply the concentration in mol/dm³ by the <u>relative formula mass</u> of the solute.
Divide by M_r to convert from g/dm³ to mol/dm³.

For the example above, M_r of NaOH = 23.0 + 16.0 + 1.0 = 40.0
So, the concentration of the solution in g/dm³ = 0.166... × 40.0 = 6.666... g/dm³ = 6.67 g/dm³.

Titration calculations require maths and concentration...

Holy moley, what a lot of numbers. Have a peek at page 31 if you need a reminder about all that M_r stuff.

Q1 27 cm³ of 0.50 mol/dm³ hydrochloric acid neutralises 15 cm³ of sodium hydroxide solution. The equation is: $HCl + NaOH \rightarrow NaCl + H_2O$. Find the concentration of the sodium hydroxide in mol/dm³. [3 marks]

Topic C5 — Monitoring and Controlling Chemical Reactions

Calculations with Gases

When dealing with <u>gases</u>, it's not appropriate to use concentration... Oh no. With gases, you're better off using <u>volume</u>. Time to meet my old friend the <u>molar volume</u> (you're going to love him, just you wait)...

Molar Volume is the Volume Occupied by One Mole of Gas

1) The volume occupied by <u>one mole of a gas</u> is known as the <u>molar volume</u>.
2) It usually has units of <u>dm³/mol</u> (dm³ per mole).
3) Here's the <u>formula</u> for calculating <u>molar volume</u>:

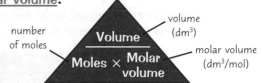

> molar volume = gas volume ÷ number of moles

EXAMPLE: Under certain conditions, 1440 cm³ of nitrogen gas, N_2, was found to have a mass of 1.80 g. What is the molar volume of nitrogen in dm³/mol under these conditions?

1) Work out how many <u>moles</u> of nitrogen gas are in 1.80 g.

moles = mass ÷ M_r
moles = 1.80 ÷ (2 × 14.0) = 0.0642... mol

2) Put the <u>volume</u> into the <u>correct units</u>.

1440 cm³ = (1440 ÷ 1000) dm³ = 1.44 dm³

3) Substitute the moles and volume into the equation to find the <u>molar volume</u>.

molar volume = volume ÷ number of moles
= 1.44 ÷ 0.0642... = 22.4 dm³/mol

Molar Volumes are the Same Under the Same Conditions

Under the same conditions, the same number of moles of different gases all occupy the <u>same volume</u>.

> One mole of any gas always occupies 24 dm³ (= 24 000 cm³) at room temperature and pressure (RTP = 20 °C and 1 atmosphere).

So, at RTP, all gases have the same <u>molar volume</u> — 24 dm³/mol.

EXAMPLE: What's the volume of 4.50 moles of chlorine at RTP?

1 mole = 24 dm³, so
4.50 moles = 4.50 × 24 dm³ = 108 dm³

EXAMPLE: How many moles are there in 8280 cm³ of hydrogen gas at RTP?

1) Make sure everything is in the <u>right units</u>. You need to convert the volume into dm³.

1000 cm³ = 1 dm³
So, 8280 cm³ = 8280 ÷ 1000 = 8.28 dm³

2) <u>Rearrange the formula</u> linking volume, number of moles and the volume of one mole (24 dm³) to get <u>number of moles</u> on its own.

Number of moles = volume of gas ÷ 24

3) Substitute your values into the rearranged equation.

Number of moles = 8.28 ÷ 24 = 0.345 moles

Memoirs of a Tooth Fairy — my favourite molar volume...

Don't let molar volumes ruin your life — they're really not that bad. Just remember that magic number, 24, and all will be fine. Here are some practice questions to make sure you've got this page nailed...

Q1 2.394 g of argon gas (Ar) takes up a volume of 1.32 dm³. What is the molar volume of argon under these conditions? [2 marks]

Q2 The M_r of methane (CH_4) is 16.0. What volume will 36 g of methane gas occupy at RTP? [2 marks]

Percentage Yield

Percentage yield tells you about the overall success of an experiment. It compares what you calculate you should get (theoretical yield) with what you get in practice (actual yield).

Percentage Yield Compares Actual and Predicted Yield

1) The amount of product you get from a reaction is known as the yield. The more reactants you start with, the higher the actual yield will be — that's pretty obvious. But the percentage yield doesn't depend on the amount of reactants you started with — it's a percentage. Percentage yield is given by the formula:

$$\text{Percentage yield} = \frac{\text{actual yield}}{\text{theoretical yield}} \times 100$$

The theoretical yield is sometimes called the predicted yield.

2) The theoretical yield of a reaction is the mass of product you'd make if all the reactants were converted to products. Theoretical yield can be calculated from the balanced reaction equation (see page 39).

EXAMPLE:

In an industrial reaction, iron oxide reacts with carbon, according to the following equation, to make iron:

$$2Fe_2O_3 + 3C \rightarrow 4Fe + 3CO_2$$

Calculate the percentage yield if you started with 50 kg of iron oxide and produced 18.9 kg of iron.

TOBY SPARKS LTD

1) Find the relative formula mass of iron oxide and the relative atomic mass of iron.

$M_r(Fe_2O_3) = (2 \times 55.8) + (3 \times 16.0) = 159.6$
$A_r(Fe) = 55.8$

2) Work out the number of moles of the reactant (iron oxide) you have.

moles = mass ÷ M_r
= (50 × 1000) ÷ 159.6
= 50 000 ÷ 159.6 = 313... moles

Convert the mass to grams: 1 kg = 1000 g

3) Use the balanced chemical equation to work out how many moles of the desired product (iron) you should end up with.

The equation tells you that 2 moles of iron oxide produces 4 moles of iron. So 313... moles of iron oxide should produce (313... ÷ 2) × 4 = 626... moles of iron.

4) Work out the theoretical yield of your desired product (iron) by converting this number of moles into mass.

mass = moles × A_r
= 626... × 55.8
= 34 962... g = 34.9... kg

Make sure your theoretical yield and your actual yield are in the same units.

5) Finally, pop the numbers into the formula to find the percentage yield.

percentage yield = $\frac{\text{actual yield}}{\text{theoretical yield}} \times 100$
= $\frac{18.9}{34.9...} \times 100 = $ **54%**

3) Percentage yield is always somewhere between 0 and 100%. A 100% percentage yield means that you got all the product you expected to get. A 0% yield means that no reactants were converted into product, i.e. no product at all was made.

4) In a reaction with a low percentage yield, a lot of the reactants will be wasted. In industry it's important to use reactions with the highest yield possible to reduce waste and keep costs as low as possible.

There are 10 grams of virtual soil in my theoretical field...

It may seem like a load of numbers, but percentage yield is really important in industry.

Q1   In a reaction, the theoretical yield of a product is 4.0 g. The actual yield is 1.2 g.
       What is the percentage yield of the reaction?   [1 mark]

Q2   1.62 g of silver were made from 3.477 g of silver oxide during the following reaction:
       $2Ag_2O \rightarrow 4Ag + O_2$. What is the percentage yield of the reaction?   [4 marks]

Topic C5 — Monitoring and Controlling Chemical Reactions

Atom Economy

It's important in __industrial reactions__ that as much of the reactants as possible get turned into __useful products__. This depends on the __atom economy__ and the __percentage yield__ (see previous page) of the reaction.

Atom Economy is the % of Reactants Changed to Useful Products

1) A lot of reactions make __more than one product__. Some of them will be __useful__, but others will just be __waste__.

2) The __atom economy__ of a reaction tells you what percentage of the __mass of the reactants__ has been converted into your __desired product__ when manufacturing a chemical. Here's the formula:

$$\text{Atom Economy} = \frac{\text{total } M_r \text{ of desired products}}{\text{total } M_r \text{ of all products}} \times 100$$

3) __100%__ atom economy means that __all__ the atoms in the reactants have been turned into __useful__ (desired) __products__. The __higher__ the atom economy the '__greener__' the process.

__EXAMPLE:__ Hydrogen gas can be made industrially by reacting natural gas (methane) with steam.

$$CH_{4\,(g)} + H_2O_{(g)} \rightarrow CO_{(g)} + 3H_{2\,(g)}$$

Calculate the atom economy of this reaction. Give your answer to 2 significant figures.

1) Identify the __desired product__.   The desired product is hydrogen gas (H_2).

2) Work out the M_r of __all the products__.

M_r of all products = $M_r(CO) + [3 \times M_r(H_2)]$
= $(12.0 + 16.0) + [3 \times (2 \times 1.0)] = 28.0 + 6.0 = 34.0$

3) Then work out the M_r of just the __desired products__.

M_r of desired products = $3 \times M_r(H_2) = 3 \times (2 \times 1.0) = 6.0$

4) Use the formula to calculate the __atom economy__.

$\text{Atom economy} = \dfrac{\text{total } M_r \text{ of desired products}}{\text{total } M_r \text{ of all products}} \times 100$

$= \dfrac{6.0}{34.0} \times 100 = \mathbf{18\%}$

So in this reaction, 82% of the starting materials are wasted.

High Atom Economy is Better for Profits and the Environment

1) Reactions with low atom economies __use up resources__ very quickly. At the same time, they make lots of __waste__ materials that have to be __disposed__ of somehow. That tends to make these reactions __unsustainable__ — the raw materials will run out and the waste has to go somewhere.

2) For the same reasons, low atom economy reactions aren't usually __profitable__. Raw materials can be __expensive to buy__ and waste products can be expensive to __remove__ and dispose of __responsibly__.

3) One way around the problem is to find a __use__ for the waste products rather than just __throwing them away__. There's often __more than one way__ to make the product you want — so the trick is to come up with a reaction that gives __useful 'by-products'__ rather than useless ones.

4) Atom economy isn't the only factor to consider in __industry__. You also need to think about:

- The __percentage yield__ (see the previous page) of the reaction.
- The __rate of reaction__ (see the next page) — the rate of the reaction you're using must be __fast enough__ to produce the amount of product you need in a sensible amount of time.
- Whether your reaction is __reversible__ (see page 73). To keep the __yield__ of a reversible reaction high, you might need to alter the __reaction conditions__, and doing this can be __expensive__.

Atom economy — budget travel for chemists...

High atom economy = yay! High yield = yay! Useful by-products = yay! Some practice questions = ???

Q1   What is the atom economy of the following reaction, used to make hydrogen?

$$C_{(s)} + 2H_2O_{(g)} \rightarrow CO_{2\,(g)} + 2H_{2\,(g)}$$ [3 marks]

Q2   Give two reasons why a high atom economy is important in industrial reactions.   [2 marks]

Reaction Rates

Reactions can be <u>fast</u> or <u>slow</u> — you've probably already realised that. It's exciting stuff. Honest.

The Rate of Reaction is a Measure of How Fast the Reaction Happens

The <u>rate of a reaction</u> is how quickly a reaction happens. It can be observed <u>either</u> by measuring how quickly the reactants are used up or how quickly the products are formed. The <u>rate of a reaction</u> can be calculated using the following formula:

$$\text{Rate of Reaction} = \frac{\text{amount of reactant used or amount of product formed}}{\text{time}}$$

It's usually a lot easier to measure products forming.

You Can Do Experiments to Follow Reaction Rates

There are different ways that the rate of a reaction can be <u>measured</u>. Here are three examples:

Precipitation

1) This method works for any reaction where mixing <u>two see-through solutions</u> produces a <u>precipitate</u>, which <u>clouds</u> the solution.

2) You <u>mix</u> the two reactant solutions and put the flask on a piece of paper that has a <u>mark</u> on it.

3) <u>Observe</u> the mark through the mixture and measure how long it takes for the mark to be <u>obscured</u>. The <u>faster</u> it disappears, the <u>faster</u> the reaction.

4) The result is <u>subjective</u> — <u>different people</u> might not agree on <u>exactly</u> when the mark 'disappears'.

You can use this method to investigate how temperature affects the rate of the reaction between sodium thiosulfate and hydrochloric acid (which produces a yellow precipitate of sulfur). You repeat the reaction using solutions at different temperatures — use a water bath to heat both solutions to the right temperature before you mix them.

Change in Mass (Usually Gas Given Off)

1) You can measure the rate of a reaction that <u>produces a gas</u> using a <u>mass balance</u>.

2) As the gas is released, the <u>lost mass</u> is easily measured on the balance. The <u>quicker</u> the reading on the balance <u>drops</u>, the <u>faster</u> the reaction.

3) You can use your results to plot a <u>graph</u> of <u>change in mass</u> against <u>time</u>.

4) This method does release the gas produced straight into the room — so if the gas is <u>harmful</u>, you must take <u>safety precautions</u>, e.g. do the experiment in a <u>fume cupboard</u>.

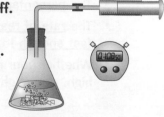

The cotton wool lets gases through but stops any solid, liquid or aqueous reactants flying out during the reaction.

The Volume of Gas Given Off

1) This involves the use of a <u>gas syringe</u> to measure the <u>volume</u> of gas given off.

2) The <u>more</u> gas given off during a set <u>time interval</u>, the <u>faster</u> the reaction.

3) You can use your results to plot a graph of <u>gas volume</u> against <u>time elapsed</u>.

4) You need to be careful that you're using the <u>right size</u> gas syringe for your experiment though — if the reaction is too <u>vigorous</u>, you can blow the plunger out of the end of the syringe.

Retraction rate — how fast my mates disappear when I tell a joke...

Lots of different ways to follow reaction rates here — well... three. Precipitation, mass loss and gas formation.

Q1 Outline how you could follow the rate of a reaction where mixing two solutions forms a precipitate. [2 marks]

Q2 Give one possible problem with using the change in mass method to follow the rate of a reaction. [1 mark]

Topic C5 — Monitoring and Controlling Chemical Reactions

Rate Experiments

PRACTICAL

You'll probably have to <u>measure</u> the <u>rate of a reaction</u> in class at some point. Time to learn how to do it...

Reaction of Hydrochloric Acid and Marble Chips

You can use this experiment to show how <u>surface area</u> affects reaction <u>rate</u>.

1) Set the apparatus up as shown in the diagram on the right.

2) Measure the <u>volume</u> of gas produced using a <u>gas syringe</u>. Take readings at <u>regular time intervals</u> and record your results in a table.

3) You can plot a <u>graph</u> of your results — time goes on the <u>x-axis</u> and <u>volume</u> goes on the <u>y-axis</u>.

4) <u>Repeat</u> the experiment with <u>exactly the same volume</u> and <u>concentration</u> of acid, and <u>exactly the same mass</u> of marble chips, but with the marble <u>more crunched up</u>.

5) Then <u>repeat</u> with the same mass of <u>powdered chalk</u>.

It's important your system is air tight so no gas escapes.

CO_2 gas
dilute HCl
marble chips ($CaCO_3$)

Marble and chalk are both made of calcium carbonate ($CaCO_3$).

Finer Particles of Solid Mean a Higher Rate

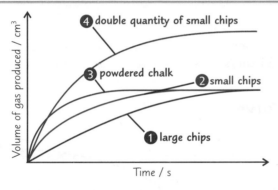

4 double quantity of small chips
3 powdered chalk
2 small chips
1 large chips
Volume of gas produced / cm³
Time / s

1) Using <u>finer particles</u> means that the marble has a <u>larger surface area</u>.

2) <u>Lines 1 to 3</u> on the graph on the left show that the <u>finer</u> the particles are (and the <u>greater</u> the surface area of the solid reactants), the <u>faster</u> the reaction goes.

3) <u>Line 4</u> shows the reaction if a <u>greater mass</u> of small marble chips is added. The <u>extra surface area</u> gives a <u>faster reaction</u> and there is also <u>more gas evolved</u> overall.

Reaction of Magnesium Metal with Dilute HCl

1) <u>This reaction</u> is good for measuring the effects of <u>changing the concentration</u> on reaction rate.

2) The reaction gives off <u>hydrogen gas</u>, so you can measure the loss of mass as the gas is formed using a <u>mass balance</u>.

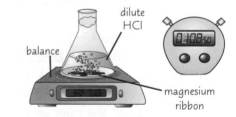
dilute HCl
balance
magnesium ribbon

More Concentrated Solutions Mean a Higher Rate

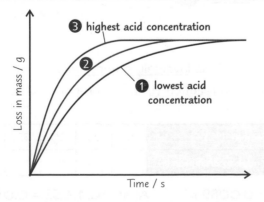

3 highest acid concentration
2
1 lowest acid concentration
Loss in mass / g
Time / s

1) During the experiment, take <u>readings</u> of the mass of the flask and its contents at <u>regular</u> time intervals. Put the results in a <u>table</u> and work out the <u>loss in mass</u> for each reading.

2) You can plot a <u>graph</u> of your results with <u>time</u> on the <u>x-axis</u> and <u>loss in mass</u> on the <u>y-axis</u>.

3) <u>Repeat</u> the experiment with <u>exactly the same mass</u> and <u>surface area</u> of magnesium and <u>exactly the same volume</u> of acid, but using different <u>concentrations</u> of acid.

4) <u>Lines 1 to 3</u> on the graph show that a <u>higher</u> concentration gives a <u>faster reaction</u>, with the reaction <u>finishing</u> sooner.

I prefer chalk to marble chips — I like the finer things in life...

Doing rate experiments lets you collect data. Collecting data lets you plot graphs, and you can use graphs to find reaction rates. But more about that on the next page. I bet you're just itching to read on...

Q1   Describe how you could investigate how the rate of reaction between magnesium and hydrochloric acid varies with the surface area of the sample of magnesium.   [3 marks]

Topic C5 — Monitoring and Controlling Chemical Reactions

Calculating Rates

You can work out rates of reaction using <u>graphs</u> or <u>tables</u>. The choice is yours (well, it's the examiner's really).

Faster Rates of Reaction are Shown by Steeper Gradients

If you have a graph of <u>amount of product formed</u> (or <u>reactant used up</u>) against <u>time</u>, then the <u>gradient</u> (slope) of the graph will be equal to the rate of the reaction — the <u>steeper</u> the slope, the <u>faster</u> the rate.

The gradient of a <u>straight line</u> is given by the equation:

$$\text{gradient} = \text{change in } y \div \text{change in } x$$

EXAMPLE:

Calculate the rate of the reaction shown on the graph on the right.

1) Find two <u>points on the line</u> that are <u>easy to read</u> the x and y values of (ones that pass through grid lines).

2) Draw a line straight <u>down</u> from the higher point and straight <u>across</u> from the lower one to make a <u>triangle</u>.

3) The <u>height</u> of your triangle = <u>change in y</u>
The <u>base</u> of your triangle = <u>change in x</u>
Change in y = 16 − 5 = 11
Change in x = 65 − 20 = 45

4) Use the formula to work out the <u>gradient</u>, and therefore the rate.
Gradient = change in y ÷ change in x = 11 ÷ 45 = 0.24 cm³/s

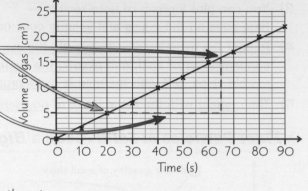

The units of the rate are just 'units of y-axis ÷ units of x-axis'.

Draw a Tangent to Find the Gradient of a Curve

1) If your graph (or part of it) is a <u>curve</u>, then the gradient, and therefore the <u>rate</u>, is different at different points along the curve.

2) To find the <u>gradient</u> of the graph at a certain point, you'll have to draw a <u>tangent</u> at that point.

3) A tangent is just a line that <u>touches the curve</u> and has the <u>same gradient</u> as the curve at that point.

4) To draw a tangent, place a <u>ruler</u> on the line of best fit at the point you're interested in, so you can see the <u>whole curve</u>. Adjust the ruler so the space between the ruler and the curve is the same on both sides of the point. Draw a line <u>along the ruler</u> to make the <u>tangent</u>.

5) The rate at that point is then just the <u>gradient</u> of the <u>tangent</u>.

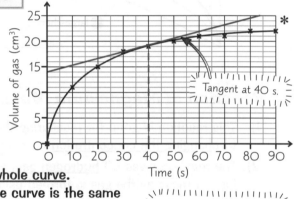

Tangent at 40 s.

A tangent is a straight line, so you can find its gradient using the straight line method shown above.

1 ÷ Time is Proportional to Rate

1) The <u>longer</u> something takes, the <u>slower</u> the <u>rate</u>. Therefore, rate is <u>inversely proportional</u> to time.

2) You can use <u>1/time</u> (or 1 ÷ time) as a measure of the rate of a reaction (1/time is proportional to rate).

EXAMPLE:

Use the table on the right to calculate the relative rate of reaction at each temperature.

Temperature (°C)	20	25	30	35	40
Time taken for mark to disappear (s)	193	151	112	87	52

At 20 °C, 1 ÷ 193 = 0.0052 s⁻¹   At 30 °C, 1 ÷ 112 = 0.0089 s⁻¹   At 40 °C, 1 ÷ 52 = 0.019 s⁻¹

At 25 °C, 1 ÷ 151 = 0.0066 s⁻¹   At 35 °C, 1 ÷ 87 = 0.011 s⁻¹

My interest in gradients is inversely proportional to time...

Lots of nifty graph skills here. Gradients aren't too hard, but make sure those tangents don't trip you up.

Q1   Work out the rate of reaction at 20 seconds using the graph (marked *) shown above.   [2 marks]

Collision Theory

The rate of a reaction depends on these things — <u>temperature</u>, <u>concentration</u> (or <u>pressure</u> for gases) and the <u>size of the particles</u> (for solids). This page explains why these things affect the reaction rate. Let's get cracking.

Particles Must Collide with Enough Energy in Order to React

<u>Reaction rates</u> are explained by <u>collision theory</u>. It's simple really.

<u>The rate of a chemical reaction</u> depends on:

- The <u>collision frequency</u> of reacting particles (<u>how often they collide</u>). The <u>more</u> successful collisions there are, the <u>faster</u> the reaction is.

- The <u>energy transferred</u> during a collision. Particles have to collide with <u>enough energy</u> for the collision to be <u>successful</u>.

A successful collision is a collision that ends in the particles reacting to form products.

The More Successful Collisions, the Higher the Rate of Reaction

Reactions happen if <u>particles collide</u>. So if you <u>increase</u> the <u>number</u> of collisions, the reaction happens <u>more quickly</u> (i.e. the rate increases). The three factors below all lead to more collisions...

Increasing the Temperature Increases Rate

1) When the <u>temperature is increased</u> the particles <u>move faster</u>. If they move faster, they're going to have <u>more collisions</u>.

2) Higher temperatures also increase the <u>energy</u> of the collisions, since the particles are moving <u>faster</u>. Reactions <u>only happen</u> if the particles collide with <u>enough energy</u>.

3) This means that at <u>higher</u> temperatures there will be more <u>successful collisions</u> (<u>more particles</u> will <u>collide</u> with <u>enough energy</u> to react). So <u>increasing</u> the temperature <u>increases</u> the rate of reaction.

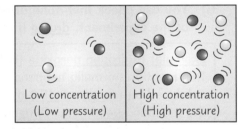

Cold   Hot

Increasing Concentration (or Pressure) Increases Rate

1) If a <u>solution</u> is made more <u>concentrated</u>, it means there are more particles of <u>reactant</u> in the same volume. This makes collisions <u>more likely</u>, so the reaction rate <u>increases</u>.

2) In a <u>gas</u>, increasing the <u>pressure</u> means that the particles are <u>more crowded</u>. This means that the frequency of <u>collisions</u> between particles will <u>increase</u> — so the rate of reaction will also <u>increase</u>.

Low concentration (Low pressure)   High concentration (High pressure)

Smaller Solid Particles (or More Surface Area) Means a Higher Rate

1) If one reactant is a <u>solid</u>, breaking it into <u>smaller</u> pieces will <u>increase its surface area to volume ratio</u> (i.e. more of the solid will be exposed, compared to its overall volume).

2) The particles around it will have <u>more area to work on</u>, so the frequency of collisions will <u>increase</u>.

3) This means that the rate of reaction is faster for solids with a larger <u>surface area to volume</u> ratio.

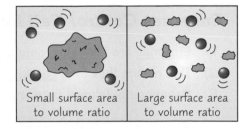

Small surface area to volume ratio   Large surface area to volume ratio

Collision theory — it's always the other driver...

Remember — more collisions mean a faster reaction. But don't be fooled, not every collision results in a reaction. The particles have to collide with enough energy to react (otherwise known as the 'activation energy').

Q1   Would you expect the rate of reaction between hydrochloric acid and calcium carbonate to be faster with calcium carbonate in the form of powder or chips? Explain your answer.   [3 marks]

Q2   Why does raising the temperature increase the rate of a reaction?   [3 marks]

Catalysts

Catalysts are very important for commercial reasons — they increase reaction rate and reduce energy costs in industrial reactions. If that's not reason enough to learn this page, I don't know what is. (Oh, apart from "exams"...)

A Catalyst Increases the Rate of a Reaction

1) A catalyst is a substance which increases the rate of a reaction, without being chemically changed or used up in the reaction.

2) Because it isn't used up, you only need a tiny bit to catalyse large amounts of reactants.

3) Catalysts tend to be very fussy about which reactions they catalyse though — you can't just stick any old catalyst in a reaction and expect it to work.

4) Catalysts work by decreasing the activation energy (see page 41) needed for a reaction to occur.

5) They do this by providing an alternative reaction pathway that has a lower activation energy.

6) You can see this if you look at a reaction profile.

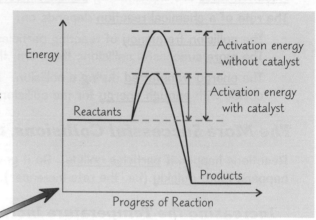

You can Identify Catalysts in Chemical Reactions

1) To find out if a substance is a catalyst for a reaction, you can do an experiment.

2) For example, if you have a solid that you think might be a catalyst for a reaction between two solutions, you could measure the reaction rate without the solid present, and then again with a known mass of the solid added.

3) If the rate increases, but the solid appears to be unchanged, it could be a catalyst.

4) To make it a fair test, you need to keep everything else the same, so that nothing else can affect the rate of reaction — that means volumes and concentrations of solutions, and the temperature.

5) You can check that none of the solid has been used up by filtering it out at the end of the experiment, drying it and measuring the mass to check it's all still there.

> Example: Hydrogen peroxide (H_2O_2) decomposes into water and oxygen: $2H_2O_2 \longrightarrow 2H_2O + O_2$.
> This reaction normally happens very slowly (so slowly that it's hard to record a rate at all). But it's catalysed by manganese(IV) oxide (MnO_2) — if you add MnO_2 powder to hydrogen peroxide solution, the reaction speeds up. Oxygen gas is given off, so you can measure the rate of reaction using the gas syringe method (see page 68). When the reaction is finished (i.e. when no more bubbles of O_2 are being given off), the appearance and the mass of the black MnO_2 powder are both unchanged.

Enzymes Control Cell Reactions

1) Enzymes are biological catalysts.

2) This means that they catalyse (speed up) the chemical reactions in living cells.

3) Reactions catalysed by enzymes include respiration, photosynthesis and protein synthesis.

Catalysts are chemical stars — but success won't change them...

There's a more fun version of that H_2O_2 experiment involving washing up liquid. If you've not seen it, ask your teacher to give a demonstration of the 'elephant's toothpaste' reaction. You won't regret it.

Q1   What is a catalyst? [2 marks]

Q2   A student adds some dark brown lead dioxide (PbO_2) powder to a flask of hydrogen peroxide solution. Lead dioxide is a catalyst for the decomposition of hydrogen peroxide. With reference to the catalyst, describe what you would expect to see in the flask after the decomposition reaction had finished. [1 mark]

Dynamic Equilibrium

<u>Reversible reactions</u> — products forming from reactants and reactants forming from products. I can't keep up...

Reversible Reactions can go Forwards and Backwards

A <u>reversible reaction</u> is one where the <u>products</u> can react with each other to produce the original <u>reactants</u>. In other words, <u>it can go both ways</u>.

$$A + B \rightleftharpoons C + D$$

The '$\rightleftharpoons$' shows the reaction goes both ways.

Reversible Reactions Will Reach Equilibrium

1) As the <u>reactants</u> (A and B) react, their <u>concentrations fall</u> — so the <u>forward reaction</u> will <u>slow down</u>. But as more and more of the <u>products</u> (C and D) are made and their <u>concentrations rise</u>, the <u>backward reaction</u> will <u>speed up</u>.

2) After a while the forward reaction will be going at <u>exactly</u> the <u>same rate</u> as the backward one — this is <u>equilibrium</u>.

3) At equilibrium <u>both</u> reactions are still <u>happening</u>, but there's <u>no overall effect</u> — it's a <u>dynamic equilibrium</u>. This means the <u>concentrations</u> of reactants and products have reached a balance and <u>won't change</u>.

4) Equilibrium can only be reached if the reversible reaction takes place in a '<u>closed system</u>'. A <u>closed system</u> just means that none of the reactants or products can <u>escape</u>.

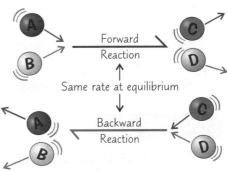

Forward Reaction

Same rate at equilibrium

Backward Reaction

The Position of Equilibrium Can be on the Right or the Left

When a reaction's at equilibrium it <u>doesn't</u> mean the amounts of reactants and products are <u>equal</u>.

1) Sometimes the equilibrium will <u>lie to the right</u> — this basically means '<u>lots of the products and not much of the reactants</u>' (i.e. the concentration of products is greater than the concentration of reactants).

2) Sometimes the equilibrium will <u>lie to the left</u> — this basically means '<u>lots of the reactants but not much of the products</u>' (the concentration of reactants is greater than the concentration of products).

3) The exact <u>position of equilibrium</u> depends on the <u>conditions</u> (as well as the reaction itself).

Three Things Can Change the Position of Equilibrium

The plural of equilibrium is 'equilibria'.

These three things can <u>change</u> the <u>position of equilibrium</u> (which changes the amounts of products and reactants present at equilibrium):

1) Temperature
2) Pressure
   (only affects equilibria involving gases)
3) Concentration

Dynamic equilibrium — lots of activity, but not to any great effect*...

Keep an eagle eye out for that arrow that shows you that a reaction is reversible. I'd hate you to miss it.

Q1 Explain what is meant by the term 'reversible reaction'. [1 mark]

Q2 What is dynamic equilibrium? [1 mark]

Q3 Name three things which can affect the position of equilibrium. [3 marks]

*Much like the England football team...

Le Chatelier's Principle

This stuff might feel a bit complicated to start with, but it all comes down to one simple rule — whatever you do to a <u>reversible reaction</u>, the <u>equilibrium position</u> will <u>move</u> to try to <u>undo</u> your change. How contrary...

The Equilibrium Position Moves to Minimise Any Changes You Make

<u>Le Chatelier's principle</u> states that if there's a <u>change</u> in concentration, pressure or temperature in a reversible reaction, the <u>equilibrium position will move</u> to help <u>counteract</u> that change.

TEMPERATURE All reactions are <u>exothermic</u> in one direction and <u>endothermic</u> in the other (see page 41).

1) If you <u>decrease the temperature</u>, the equilibrium will move in the <u>exothermic direction</u> to produce more heat.

2) If you <u>increase the temperature</u>, the equilibrium will move in the <u>endothermic direction</u> to absorb the extra heat.

> For example: $N_2 + 3H_2 \rightleftharpoons 2NH_3$
> This reaction is exothermic in the forward direction. If you decrease the temperature, the equilibrium will shift to the right (so you'll make more product).

PRESSURE Changing this only affects equilibria involving <u>gases</u>.

1) If you <u>increase the pressure</u>, the equilibrium will move towards the side that has <u>fewer moles of gas</u> to <u>reduce</u> pressure.

2) If you <u>decrease the pressure</u>, the equilibrium will move towards the side that has <u>more moles of gas</u> to <u>increase</u> pressure.

> For example:
> $N_2 + 3H_2 \rightleftharpoons 2NH_3$
> This reaction has 4 moles of gas on the left and 2 on the right. If you increase the pressure, the equilibrium will shift to the right (so you'll make more product).

CONCENTRATION

1) If you <u>increase the concentration</u> of the <u>reactants</u>, the equilibrium will move to the <u>right</u> to <u>use up the reactants</u> (making <u>more products</u>).

2) If you <u>increase the concentration</u> of the <u>products</u>, the equilibrium will move to the <u>left</u> to <u>use up the products</u> (making <u>more reactants</u>).

3) <u>Decreasing</u> the concentrations will have the <u>opposite effect</u>.

> For example:
> $N_2 + 3H_2 \rightleftharpoons 2NH_3$
> If you increase the concentration of N_2 or H_2, the equilibrium will shift to the right to use up the extra reactants (so you'll make more product).

You Can Predict How the Position of Equilibrium Will Change

You can apply the rules above to any reversible reaction to work out how <u>changing the conditions</u> will affect the <u>equilibrium position</u>. This has useful applications in <u>industry</u> — you can <u>increase yield</u> (see page 66) by changing the conditions to shift the equilibrium position to the <u>right</u> (towards the <u>products</u>).

> The Haber Process (see page 80) and the Contact Process (see page 82) both use reversible reactions.

 **EXAMPLE:**

The compound PCl_5 can be made using this reaction: $PCl_{3\,(g)} + Cl_{2\,(g)} \rightleftharpoons PCl_{5\,(g)}$
Explain what would happen to the equilibrium position and to the yield of PCl_5 if you increased the pressure that the reaction was being performed at.

According to Le Chatelier's Principle, if you increase the pressure, the position of equilibrium will move towards the side with fewer moles of gas to reduce the pressure. In this reaction there are 2 moles of gas in the reactants and 1 in the products. The position of equilibrium will move to the right, since that is the side with fewer moles of gas. This shifts the equilibrium towards the products, so the yield of PCl_5 will increase.

Le Chatelier — relieving pressure since 1884...

Le Chatelier's principle may relieve the pressure in chemical systems, but it stands a chance of giving you a right headache in the exam. So, best make sure you understand it now by trying these questions...

Q1   This reaction is endothermic in the forward direction: $CH_3OH_{(g)} \rightleftharpoons CO_{(g)} + 2H_{2\,(g)}$. What will happen to the position of equilibrium if the temperature is increased? Explain your answer.   [2 marks]

Q2   What would happen to the yield of SO_3 in the reaction below if the pressure was decreased? Explain your answer. $2SO_{2\,(g)} + O_{2\,(g)} \rightleftharpoons 2SO_{3\,(g)}$ [3 marks]

Revision Questions for Topic C5

Wasn't that fun? I liked the maths best, but that might just be me... Time to test your knowledge of Topic C5.
*   Try these questions and tick off each one when you get it right.
*   When you've done all the questions under a heading and are completely happy with it, tick it off.

Concentration and Titrations (p.63-64) ☑

1) Give the formula that links concentration, volume of solution and mass of solute. ☑
2) Describe the technique for making up a standard solution from a solid. ☑
3) Describe how you would carry out a titration to work out the concentration of an unknown alkali. ☑
4) Write down the formula that links concentration, volume of solution and number of moles. ☑

Calculations with Gases (p.65) ☑

5) What is the 'molar volume' of a gas? ☑
6) What volume does one mole of gas occupy at room temperature and pressure? ☑

Percentage Yield and Atom Economy (p.66-67) ☐

7) What formula would you use to work out the percentage yield of a reaction? ☑
8) What formula would you use to work out the atom economy of a reaction? ☑
9) Why aren't reactions with low atom economies usually profitable? ☑

Rates of Reactions (p.68-70) ☑

10) What is the 'rate' of a reaction? ☑
11) Describe how you would set up an experiment to follow the rate
    of a reaction by measuring the volume of gas that it produced. ☑
12) Imagine you have drawn a results graph for a rate of reaction experiment. The graph is a curve.
    Describe how you could find the rate of a reaction at a certain time point using the graph. ☑

Collision Theory (p.71) ☐

13) State how the frequency of successful collisions affects the rate of a reaction. ☑
14) How does increasing the pressure of a reaction involving gases affect the rate of a reaction? ☑

Catalysts (p.72) ☑

15) Sketch a reaction profile showing an uncatalysed reaction and the same reaction with a catalyst added. ☐
16) What is an enzyme? ☑

Dynamic Equilibrium (p.73) ☑

17) Draw the symbol which shows that a reaction is reversible. ☑
18) What is a closed system? ☑
19) If the position of equilibrium for a reversible reaction lies to the right,
    what does that tell you about the relative amounts of reactants and products present? ☑

Le Chatelier's Principle (p.64) ☑

20) State Le Chatelier's principle. ☑
21) Describe what would happen to the equilibrium position of a reversible reaction
    if you increased the concentration of the reactants. ☑

Extracting Metals from their Ores

A few <u>unreactive metals</u>, like gold, are found in the Earth as the metal itself, rather than as a compound. The rest of the metals we get by <u>extracting</u> them <u>from rocks</u> — and I bet you're just itching to find out how...

Ores Contain Enough Metal to Make Extraction Worthwhile

A <u>metal ore</u> is a <u>rock</u> which contains <u>enough metal</u> to make it <u>economically worthwhile</u> extracting the metal from it. In many cases the ore is an <u>oxide</u> of the metal. For example, the main <u>aluminium ore</u> is called <u>bauxite</u> — it's aluminium oxide (Al_2O_3).

Metals Are Extracted From their Ores Chemically

1) A metal can be extracted from its ore <u>chemically</u> — by <u>reduction</u> (see below) or by <u>electrolysis</u> (splitting with electricity, see pages 47-49).

2) Some ores may have to be <u>concentrated</u> before the metal is extracted — this just involves getting rid of the <u>unwanted rocky material</u>.

3) <u>Electrolysis</u> can also be used to <u>purify</u> the extracted metal (see next page).

4) There are other ways to extract metals though. Some metals are extracted from their ores using <u>displacement reactions</u> (see page 57), or by using <u>biological methods</u> (see the next page).

Row faster men!

We can't — it's these cursed metal oars.

Some Metals can be Extracted by Reduction with Carbon

1) A metal can be <u>extracted</u> from its ore chemically by <u>reduction</u> using <u>carbon</u>.

2) When an ore is reduced, <u>oxygen is removed</u> from it, e.g.

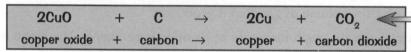

$$2CuO \quad + \quad C \quad \rightarrow \quad 2Cu \quad + \quad CO_2$$
$$\text{copper oxide} \quad + \quad \text{carbon} \quad \rightarrow \quad \text{copper} \quad + \quad \text{carbon dioxide}$$

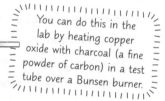

You can do this in the lab by heating copper oxide with charcoal (a fine powder of carbon) in a test tube over a Bunsen burner.

3) The position of the metal in the <u>reactivity series</u> determines whether it can be extracted by <u>reduction</u> with carbon.

See page 57 for more on reactivity series.

- Metals <u>higher than carbon</u> in the reactivity series have to be extracted using <u>electrolysis</u> (see next page) which is expensive.

- Metals <u>below carbon</u> in the reactivity series can be extracted by <u>reduction</u> using <u>carbon</u>. For example, <u>iron oxide</u> is reduced in a <u>blast furnace</u> to make <u>iron</u>.

- This is because carbon <u>can only take the oxygen</u> away from metals which are <u>less reactive</u> than carbon <u>itself</u> is.

The Reactivity Series		
Potassium	K	more reactive
Sodium	Na	
Calcium	Ca	
Magnesium	Mg	
Aluminium	Al	
<u>CARBON</u>	<u>C</u>	
Zinc	Zn	
Iron	Fe	
Tin	Sn	
Copper	Cu	less reactive

Extracted using electrolysis

Extracted by reduction using carbon

[Please insert ore-ful pun here]...

Make sure you've got that reactivity series sorted in your head. If a metal's below carbon in the reactivity series, then it's less reactive than carbon and can be extracted from its ore by reduction using carbon. Phew... got it?

Q1   How would you extract tin from its metal ore? Explain your answer.   [2 marks]

Q2   Write a balanced chemical equation to describe the reaction that occurs when carbon is used to extract zinc from its ore, zinc oxide (ZnO).   [2 marks]

Extracting Metals with Electrolysis

Electrolysis is an expensive process, but like many pricey things it's really rather good...

Some Metals have to be Extracted by Electrolysis

1) Metals that are more reactive than carbon (see previous page) are extracted using electrolysis of molten compounds (see page 48 for more on this).

The compounds have to be molten (i.e. liquid) so that the electrons and ions are free to move.

2) Once the metal is melted, an electric current is passed through it. The metal is discharged at the cathode and the non-metal at the anode.

3) Electricity is expensive so this process is much more expensive than reduction with carbon.

> Example: When aluminium is extracted from its ore, aluminium oxide, the ore is first dissolved in molten cryolite (an aluminium compound) so the ions in the ore are free to move. During the electrolysis, aluminium is formed at the cathode where it sinks to the bottom of the cell and is siphoned off. Oxygen forms at the anode.

Copper is Purified by Electrolysis

1) Copper can be easily extracted by reduction with carbon (see previous page). The ore is heated in a furnace — this is called smelting.

2) However, the copper produced this way is impure — and impure copper doesn't conduct electricity very well. This isn't very useful because a lot of copper is used to make electrical wiring.

3) So electrolysis is also used to purify it, even though it's quite expensive.

4) This produces very pure copper, which is a much better conductor.

The negative electrode (cathode) starts as a thin piece of pure copper and more pure copper adds to it.

The positive electrode (anode) is just a big lump of impure copper, which will dissolve.

The electrolyte is copper sulfate solution containing Cu^{2+} ions.

sludge

We can also recycle metals to save resources (see page 85).

There are Biological Methods to Extract Metals

1) The supply of some metal rich ores, e.g. copper ore, is limited.

2) The demand for lots of metals is growing and this may lead to shortages in the future.

3) Scientists are looking into new ways of extracting metals from low-grade ores (ores that only contain small amounts of the metal) or from the waste that is currently produced when metals are extracted.

4) Examples of new methods to extract metals from their ores are bioleaching and phytoextraction. These are biological methods as they use living organisms.

> Bioleaching: This uses bacteria to separate metals from their ores, e.g. copper can be separated from copper sulfide this way. The bacteria get energy from the bonds between the atoms in the ore, separating out the metal from the ore in the process. The leachate (the solution produced by the process) contains metal ions, which can be extracted, e.g. by electrolysis (see p.47-49) or displacement (see p.57) with a more reactive metal.

> Phytoextraction: This involves growing plants in soil that contains metal compounds. The plants can't use or get rid of the metals so they gradually build up in the leaves. The plants can be harvested, dried and burned in a furnace. The ash contains metal compounds from which the metal can be extracted by electrolysis or displacement reactions.

5) Traditional methods of mining are pretty damaging to the environment (see page 85). These new methods of extraction have a much smaller impact, but the disadvantage is that they're slow.

A policeman failed his maths test — he's a low-grade copper...

More electrolysis? It's just cropping up everywhere. That means there's no excuse not to know it.

Q1   Draw and label a diagram to show how copper is purified using electrolysis.   [3 marks]

Q2   Name and describe two ways copper can be extracted from low-grade ores.   [4 marks]

Alloys

Different metals have <u>different properties</u>. But, by combining them with other elements you can create a new material that keeps some of the properties of the original materials, and has some <u>extra properties</u> too.

An Alloy is a Mixture of a Metal and Other Elements

1) Alloys can be a mixture of <u>two or more different metals</u>.
   Brass and bronze (see below) are examples of alloys made up of two different metals.

2) They can also be a mixture of a <u>metal and a non-metal</u> (like steel).

3) Alloys often have properties that are <u>different</u> from the metals they're made from
   — and these new properties often make the alloy <u>more useful</u> than the pure metal.

You first met alloys back on page 24.

Steel is an Alloy of Iron and Carbon

1) Steel is <u>harder</u> than iron.

2) Steel is also <u>stronger</u> than iron, as long as the amount of carbon does not get greater than about 1%.

3) Iron on its own will <u>rust</u> (<u>corrode</u>) fairly quickly, but steel is much less likely to rust.
   A small amount of carbon makes a big difference.

4) A lot of things are <u>made from steel</u> — girders, bridges, engine parts,
   cutlery, washing machines, saucepans, ships, drill bits, cars, etc.

Brass, Bronze, Solder and Duralumin are also Alloys

BRASS

<u>Brass</u> is an alloy of <u>copper</u> and <u>zinc</u>. Most of the <u>properties</u> of brass are just a <u>mixture</u> of those of the copper and zinc, although brass is <u>harder</u> than either of them.
Brass is used for making brass <u>musical instruments</u> (trumpets, trombones, French horns etc.).
It's also used for <u>fixtures and fittings</u> such as screws, springs, doorknobs, etc.

BRONZE

<u>Bronze</u> is an alloy of <u>copper</u> and <u>tin</u>. It's much harder and stronger than tin, and it's more resistant to corrosion than either copper or tin. Bronze is used to make <u>springs</u> and <u>motor bearings</u>. It's also used to make <u>bells</u>, and it's used in <u>sculpture</u>.

SOLDER

<u>Solder</u> is usually an alloy of <u>lead</u> and <u>tin</u>. Unlike <u>pure</u> materials it doesn't have a definite melting point, but <u>gradually</u> solidifies as it cools down.
This makes solder pretty useful for <u>joining</u> metal things together as it can be easily worked — for example, it's used to connect <u>components</u> in <u>electronic circuits</u>.
It also has a relatively <u>low melting point</u> — this is useful as it means you can melt solder without deforming <u>other components</u> in the circuit.

I said solder — not soldier...

DURALUMIN

<u>Duralumin</u> is an alloy mostly composed of <u>aluminium</u> (about 94%), with small amounts of <u>copper</u> (around 4%), <u>magnesium</u> (about 1%) and often small amounts of manganese as well. It's a very <u>low density</u> alloy (i.e. for its volume, it's really light) and is much <u>stronger</u> than aluminium. Because it's strong and light, it's really useful for making parts of <u>aeroplanes</u> and other <u>aircraft</u>.

If Iron Man and the Silver Surfer teamed up, they'd be great alloys...

Life would be pretty different without alloys around. I'd have to cancel my trumpet recital for a start...

Q1   Give one use of steel.   [1 mark]

Q2   Which properties of duralumin make it good for building aircraft?   [1 mark]

Corrosion

<u>Corrosion</u> is a process where something is slowly damaged or destroyed by a chemical process. <u>Rusting</u> is a type of <u>corrosion</u>. You see it all over the place but why does it actually happen? Let's find out...

Rusting of Iron is a Redox Reaction

1) If <u>iron</u> comes into contact with air and water, after a while, it will <u>rust</u>.
   Rusting only happens when the iron's in contact with <u>both oxygen</u> (from the air) and <u>water</u>.

2) Rust is a form of <u>hydrated iron(III) oxide</u>.

3) This <u>equation</u> shows the <u>formation of rust</u>:

$$\text{iron} + \text{oxygen} + \text{water} \rightarrow \text{hydrated iron(III) oxide}$$

Only iron can form rust, but other metals can be oxidised and corrode.

4) Rusting of iron is a <u>redox reaction</u>. <u>Iron loses electrons</u> when it reacts with oxygen.
   Each Fe atom <u>loses three electrons</u> to become Fe^{3+}, so iron's <u>oxidised</u>.
   Simultaneously, <u>oxygen gains electrons</u> when it reacts with iron.
   Each O atom <u>gains two electrons</u> to become O^{2-}. Oxygen's <u>reduced</u>.

Remember OIL RIG — Oxidation is Loss, Reduction is Gain (of electrons) — see page 47.

5) Other metals can <u>corrode</u> in the presence of oxygen and water to form their metal oxides.

Oil, Grease and Paint Prevent Corrosion

1) You can <u>prevent corrosion</u> by coating the metal with a <u>barrier</u>.
   This <u>keeps out the water</u>, <u>oxygen</u> or <u>both</u>.

2) <u>Painting</u> is ideal for large and small structures. It can also be nice and <u>colourful</u>.

3) <u>Oiling</u> or <u>greasing</u> has to be used when <u>moving parts</u> are involved, like on <u>bike chains</u>.

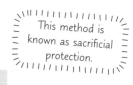

Neigh.

A Coat of Tin Will Protect Steel from Corroding

1) <u>Tin plating</u> is where a coat of tin is applied to the object, e.g. food cans.

2) The tin acts as a <u>barrier</u>, stopping water and oxygen in the air from reaching the <u>surface</u> of the metal.

3) This only works as long as the <u>tin coating remains intact</u>.
   If the tin is <u>scratched</u> to reveal some of the metal below, it will start to corrode.

More Reactive Metals Can Prevent Metals Corroding

You can also prevent corrosion using the <u>sacrificial</u> method. You place a <u>more reactive metal</u> with whatever you don't want to corrode. The water and oxygen then react with this 'sacrificial' metal instead of with the metal you're protecting.

This method is known as sacrificial protection.

1) <u>Galvanising</u> is where a coat of <u>zinc</u> is put onto an iron object to prevent rusting. The zinc acts as sacrificial protection — it's <u>more reactive</u> than iron so it'll <u>lose electrons in preference</u> to iron. The zinc also acts as a barrier. Steel <u>buckets</u> and <u>corrugated iron roofing</u> are often galvanised.

2) Blocks of metal, e.g. <u>magnesium</u>, can be bolted to less reactive metals to prevent corrosion. Magnesium <u>loses electrons</u> in preference to the <u>less reactive metal</u>. It's used on <u>ship hulls</u>, or on <u>underground pipes</u>.

My old robot friend died yesterday — may he rust in peace...

Rust gets everywhere. On my car, my old bike, now in your exam. Best get some practice in now...

Q1   How does painting a metal prevent it from corroding?   [1 mark]

Q2   Outline how bolting some magnesium onto a piece of iron will prevent it from rusting.   [2 marks]

The Haber Process

This is an important <u>industrial process</u>. It produces <u>ammonia</u> (NH_3), which is used to make fertilisers.

Nitrogen and Hydrogen Are Needed to Make Ammonia

1) The <u>Haber process</u> is used to produce <u>ammonia</u> by the following reaction:

$$N_{2\,(g)} + 3H_{2\,(g)} \rightleftharpoons 2NH_{3\,(g)} \quad (+ \text{ heat})$$

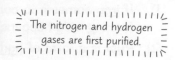
The nitrogen and hydrogen gases are first purified.

2) The <u>nitrogen</u> (N_2) is obtained easily from the <u>air</u>, which is <u>78% nitrogen</u>.

3) The <u>hydrogen</u> (H_2) can be obtained from <u>hydrocarbons</u> from sources such as <u>natural gas</u> or <u>crude oil</u>.

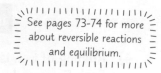
See pages 73-74 for more about reversible reactions and equilibrium.

4) Some of the nitrogen and hydrogen reacts to form <u>ammonia</u>. Because the reaction is <u>reversible</u> (it occurs in both directions) ammonia breaks down again into nitrogen and hydrogen. The reaction reaches an <u>equilibrium</u>.

The Reaction Conditions Chosen are a Compromise

1) In industry, ammonia is made at a pressure of 200 atm and a temperature of 450 °C in the presence of an iron catalyst.

2) <u>Higher pressures</u> favour the <u>forward</u> reaction (since there are four moles of gas on the left-hand side, for every two moles on the right — see the equation above).

3) So the pressure is set <u>as high as possible</u> to give the best yield (see page 74), without making the plant too expensive to build (it'd be too expensive to build a plant that'd stand pressures of over 1000 atmospheres, for example). Hence the <u>200 atmospheres</u> operating pressure.

4) The <u>forward reaction</u> is <u>exothermic</u>, which means that <u>increasing</u> the <u>temperature</u> will actually move the equilibrium position the <u>wrong way</u> — away from ammonia and towards nitrogen and hydrogen. So the yield of ammonia would be greater at <u>lower temperatures</u>. (See pages 73-74 for more on equilibrium.)

5) The trouble is, <u>lower temperatures</u> mean a <u>lower rate of reaction</u>. So in industry, the temperature is increased anyway, to get a much faster rate of reaction.

6) The 450 ºC is a <u>compromise</u> between <u>maximum yield</u> and <u>speed of reaction</u>. It's better to wait just <u>20 seconds</u> for a <u>10% yield</u> than to have to wait <u>60 seconds</u> for a <u>20% yield</u>.

7) The <u>ammonia</u> is formed as a <u>gas</u> but as it cools in the condenser it <u>liquefies</u> and is <u>removed</u>.

8) The unused hydrogen and nitrogen are <u>recycled</u> so <u>nothing is wasted</u>.

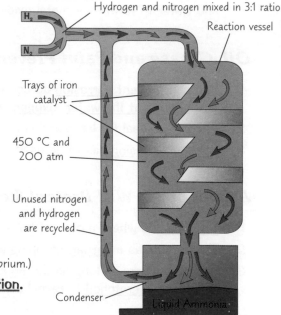
Hydrogen and nitrogen mixed in 3:1 ratio
Reaction vessel
H_2
N_2
Trays of iron catalyst
450 °C and 200 atm
Unused nitrogen and hydrogen are recycled
Condenser
Liquid Ammonia

The Iron Catalyst Speeds Up the Reaction and Reduces Costs

1) The <u>iron catalyst</u> makes the reaction go <u>faster</u>, which gets it to the <u>equilibrium proportions</u> more quickly. But remember, the catalyst <u>doesn't</u> affect the <u>position</u> of equilibrium (i.e. the % yield).

2) <u>Without the catalyst</u> the temperature would have to be <u>raised even further</u> to get a <u>quick enough</u> reaction, and that would <u>reduce the % yield</u> even further. So the catalyst is very important.

It's tricky stuff but go on, Haber go at it...

The stuff about the equilibrium position and yield is all to do with Le Chatelier's Principle, so look back at page 74 if you need a reminder on how changing reaction conditions affects the equilibrium and yield.

Q1　A pressure of 200 atm is used in the industrial production of ammonia via the Haber process.
　　What would happen to the yield of ammonia if a higher pressure was used? Explain your answer. [2 marks]

Fertilisers

There's a lot more to using <u>fertilisers</u> than making your garden look nice and pretty...

Fertilisers Help Plants Grow

1) The three main <u>essential</u> elements in fertilisers are <u>nitrogen</u>, <u>phosphorus</u> and <u>potassium</u>. Plants absorb these nutrients from the soil.

2) If plants don't get enough of these elements, their <u>growth</u> and <u>life processes</u> are affected.

3) Fertilisers <u>replace</u> these missing elements in the soil, or provide <u>more</u> of them. This helps to increase the <u>crop yield</u>, as the crops can grow <u>faster</u> and <u>bigger</u>.

Ammonia Can be Neutralised with Acids to Produce Fertilisers

Ammonia is a <u>base</u> and can be <u>neutralised</u> by acids to make <u>ammonium salts</u>.
Ammonia is really important to world food production, because it's a <u>key ingredient</u> of many <u>fertilisers</u>.

1) If you neutralise <u>nitric acid</u> with ammonia you get <u>ammonium nitrate</u>. It's an especially good fertiliser because it has a high percentage of <u>nitrogen</u>, the ammonia and the nitric acid — kind of a <u>double dose</u>.

2) <u>Ammonium sulfate</u> can also be used as a fertiliser. You make it by neutralising <u>sulfuric acid</u> (from the Contact process, see the next page) with ammonia (formed in the Haber Process — see last page).

3) <u>Ammonium phosphate</u> is a fertiliser made by neutralising <u>phosphoric acid</u> with <u>ammonia</u>.

4) <u>Potassium nitrate</u> is also a fertiliser — it can be made by neutralising <u>nitric acid</u> with <u>potassium hydroxide</u>.

A fertiliser factory will carry out several integrated processes to make fertilisers. E.g. it may make <u>ammonia</u> using the <u>Haber process</u> (see previous page), <u>phosphoric acid</u> from phosphate rock, sulfuric acid (made using the <u>Contact process</u>, see next page) or nitric acid. These chemicals are then used to make <u>ammonium phosphates</u>, <u>ammonium sulfate</u> and <u>ammonium nitrate</u>.

Preparing Ammonium Sulfate in the Lab

You can make most fertilisers using this <u>titration</u> method — just choose the right <u>acid</u> (nitric, sulfuric or phosphoric) and <u>alkali</u> (ammonia or potassium hydroxide) to get the <u>salt</u> you want. You'll need <u>ammonia</u> and <u>sulfuric acid</u> to make <u>ammonium sulfate</u>.

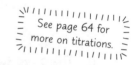
See page 64 for more on titrations.

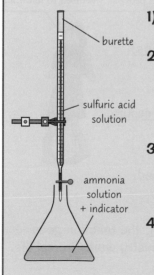

burette

sulfuric acid solution

ammonia solution + indicator

1) Set up your apparatus as in the diagram. Add a few drops of <u>methyl orange indicator</u> to the ammonia — it'll turn <u>yellow</u>.

2) <u>Slowly</u> add the sulfuric acid from the burette into the ammonia solution, until the yellow colour <u>just</u> changes to red. Gently swirl the flask as you add the acid and go especially <u>slowly</u> when you get close to the end point. Methyl orange is <u>yellow</u> in <u>alkalis</u>, but <u>red</u> in <u>acids</u>, so this <u>colour change</u> means that <u>all</u> the ammonia has been <u>neutralised</u> and you've got ammonium sulfate solution.

3) The ammonium sulfate solution isn't <u>pure</u> — it's still got <u>methyl orange</u> in it. To get <u>pure</u> ammonium sulfate crystals, you need to note <u>exactly</u> how much sulfuric acid it took to neutralise the ammonia, then repeat the titration using that volume of acid, but <u>no indicator</u>.

4) To get solid <u>ammonium sulfate crystals</u>, gently evaporate the solution (using a steam bath) until only a little bit is left. Leave it to <u>crystallise</u> then filter out the crystals and leave them to dry (see page 28).

In industry, you can't use this method as it's impractical to use burettes and steam baths for large quantities, and crystallisation is slow.

This page isn't too bad — ammonia's pretty basic stuff...

Yet another titration... It's pretty similar to the ones you met back on page 64, so no need to panic.

Q1   What is the role of a fertiliser?   [1 mark]

Q2   Name three elements that are important components in fertilisers.   [2 marks]

Q3   Describe the process for making pure ammonium sulfate crystals in the lab.   [6 marks]

The Contact Process

And here's another example where getting the __conditions right__ makes you more product. Whoop.

The Contact Process is Used to Make Sulfuric Acid

1) The first stage is to make __sulfur dioxide__ (SO_2) — usually by burning __sulfur__ in __air__.

$$\text{sulfur} + \text{oxygen} \rightarrow \text{sulfur dioxide}$$
$$S_{(s)} + O_{2(g)} \rightarrow SO_{2(g)}$$

2) The sulfur dioxide is then __oxidised__ (with the help of a catalyst) to make __sulfur trioxide__ (SO_3).

$$\text{sulfur dioxide} + \text{oxygen} \rightleftharpoons \text{sulfur trioxide}$$
$$2SO_{2(g)} + O_{2(g)} \rightleftharpoons 2SO_{3(g)}$$

3) Next, the sulfur trioxide is used to make __sulfuric acid__.

$$\text{sulfur trioxide} + \text{water} \rightarrow \text{sulfuric acid}$$
$$SO_{3(g)} + H_2O_{(l)} \rightarrow H_2SO_{4(aq)}$$

In reality, it's a bit more complicated than this — dissolving SO_3 in water is dangerous as a lot of heat's produced. In practice, you dissolve SO_3 in sulfuric acid first.

The Conditions Used to Make SO₃ are Carefully Chosen

The reaction in step 2 above is __reversible__. So, the __reaction conditions__ can be controlled to __change the equilibrium position__. The conditions used in industry for the Contact process are a __compromise__ between the __rate of reaction__ (how fast the reaction happens — see page 68), the __yield__ (how much of the reactants are converted to products — see page 66) and __cost__.

TEMPERATURE

1) Oxidising sulfur dioxide to form sulfur trioxide is __exothermic__ (it __gives out__ heat).

2) So to get a __higher yield__ of product, you'd think the temperature should be __reduced__ (so the equilibrium will shift to the __right__ to __replace the heat__).

3) Unfortunately, reducing the temperature __slows__ the reaction right down — not much good.

4) So a __compromise__ temperature of __450 °C__ is used — to get an acceptable yield quite quickly.

PRESSURE

1) There are __two moles__ of gas on the __products__ side, compared to __three moles__ of gas on the __reactants__ side.

2) So to get a __higher yield__ of product, you'd think the pressure should be __increased__ (so that the equilibrium will shift to the __right__ to __reduce the pressure__).

3) But increasing the pressure is __expensive__ (and luckily the equilibrium already lies to the right, so it's not really __necessary__).

4) In fact, the reaction is usually carried out at, or just above, __atmospheric pressure__.

This isn't the sort of contact process I wanted to learn about...

CATALYST

1) To __increase__ the rate of reaction a __vanadium pentoxide catalyst__ (V_2O_5) is used.

2) It __DOESN'T__ change the __position__ of the equilibrium.

With a __fairly high temperature__, a __low pressure__ and a __vanadium pentoxide catalyst__, the reaction goes __pretty quickly__ without reducing the yield of SO_3 too much. And that's how chemistry works in real life.

The lonely hearts column — go on, start the contact process...

It's a tough one... Do you raise the temperature to get a faster rate of reaction, or reduce it to get a better yield? In the end you just have to make a compromise (as is so often the case in life... sigh).

Q1 Write balanced chemical equations, including state symbols, to show how sulfuric acid is formed from sulfur, oxygen and water. [6 marks]

Q2 Describe how you could alter the pressure of the reaction to increase the yield of sulfur trioxide in the second stage of the synthesis of sulfuric acid. Explain your answer. [2 marks]

Topic C6 — Global Challenges

Industrial Processes

Making chemicals isn't just a case of bunging some reactants in a container and reacting them. There's lots to consider, such as how much the reactants cost, how long the products will take to make, the list goes on...

Industrial Processes Must be Economical

1) Picking the conditions to use for a chemical reaction isn't always that simple. Sometimes, the conditions that give the fastest rate may not give the highest yield (e.g. the Haber Process on page 80).

2) You also have to consider what your reactants are and where they come from. There will be cost implications depending on what the raw, starting materials are.

3) When designing an industrial process, you should consider the following things...

Raw materials are the basic materials from which your products are made.

Cost of Raw Materials

What are the starting materials of your reaction? Often you won't be able to just pull your starting materials out of the ground — they'll probably need to be refined or purified. You might even have to make them as part of another chemical reaction. How much it costs to extract, refine or make your starting materials will affect whether the process is economically viable or not. If the raw materials are too expensive to source, then the industrial manufacture of the product may not be profitable.

Availability of Raw Materials

Some raw materials, such as crude oil, are non-renewable — they'll eventually run out. When considering your starting materials and where you get them from, it's best to try and use raw materials that are renewable, or common, rather than in short supply.

Energy Costs

Energy costs are the costs associated with reaching and maintaining the conditions required for the reaction to happen (e.g. temperatures and pressures). Generally, higher temperatures and pressures cost more to maintain, so low temperatures and pressures are used wherever possible.

If you produce energy by burning fossil fuels, reducing energy costs by burning less fuel also means you produce fewer harmful emissions (see page 99).

Rate

It's no good having an industrial reaction that takes forever — you want your product to be made at a reasonable rate. This can sometimes mean compromising the yield.

Graphs can show how rate changes with reaction conditions. Sometimes the rate will keep increasing with the value of one of the reaction conditions (this happens with temperature and pressure). In other cases, there may be optimum conditions, and the rate might be very slow at other conditions. See pages 68-70 for more on reaction graphs and rate.

Catalysts (see page 72) are often used to speed up reactions.

Rate increases as temperature increases.

rate / temperature / °C

Optimum pH — at this point, the rate is the fastest.

rate / pH

Equilibrium Position

Some industrial reactions are reversible. Being able to control the position of equilibrium to maximise the amount of product made is an important part of making an industrial process profitable. If the equilibrium position lies to the left then the reaction will have a low yield (i.e. not much of the reactants are made into products) and if it's difficult or expensive to alter, then the reaction may not be viable.

You can control the concentrations of reactants, the pressure and the temperature to alter the equilibrium position of reactions (see page 74).

My rate of revision has optimum conditions...

...usually involving some highlighters, some lined paper, a large sandwich, a victoria sponge, a swiss roll...

Q1   Suggest two things you should consider when you pick the raw materials to use in industrial process.

[2 marks]

Life-Cycle Assessments

If a company wants to manufacture a new product, it will carry out a life-cycle assessment (LCA). This looks at every stage of the product's life to assess the impact it would have on the environment.

Life-cycle Assessments Show Total Environmental Costs

A life-cycle assessment (LCA) looks at each stage of the life of a product — from making the material from natural raw materials, making the product from the material, using the product and disposing of the product. It works out the potential environmental impact of each stage.

Choice of material

1) Metals have to be mined and extracted from their ores. These processes need a lot of energy and cause a lot of pollution.

2) Raw materials for chemical manufacture often come from crude oil. Crude oil is a non-renewable resource, and supplies are decreasing. Also, obtaining crude oil from the ground and refining it into useful raw materials requires a lot of energy and generates pollution.

Manufacture

1) Manufacturing products uses a lot of energy and other resources.

2) It can also cause a lot of pollution, e.g. harmful gases such as CO or HCl.

3) You also need to think about any waste products and how to dispose of them.

4) Some waste can be recycled and turned into other useful chemicals, reducing the amount that ends up polluting the environment.

5) Most chemical manufacture needs water. Businesses have to make sure they don't put polluted water back into the environment at the end of the process.

Product Use

Using the product can also damage the environment. For example:

1) Paint gives off toxic fumes.

2) Burning fuels releases greenhouse gases and other harmful substances.

3) Fertilisers can leach into streams and rivers and cause damage to ecosystems.

Disposal

1) Products are often disposed of in a landfill site at the end of their life.

2) This takes up space and can pollute land and water.

3) Products might be incinerated (burnt), which causes air pollution.

Some products can be disposed of by being recycled (see next page).

EXAMPLE:

A company is carrying out a life-cycle assessment to work out which car, A, B or C, it should make. Using the data in the table, explain which car the company should produce to minimise the environmental impact.

Car	CO_2 emissions (tonnes)	Waste solid produced (kg)	Water used (m³)	Expected lifespan of product (years)
A	17	10 720	8.2	11
B	21	5900	6.0	17
C	34	15 010	9.5	12

- Car A produces the least CO_2, but produces the second highest amount of waste solids and uses the second highest amount of water. It also has the shortest life span.

- Car B produces more CO_2 than car A, but produces by far the least waste solid, uses the least water and also has the longest life span. On balance, this looks a better choice than car A.

- Car C produces the most CO_2, the most waste solid, uses the most water, and has almost as short a life span as car A. This looks like the worst choice.

So, on balance, **car B** looks like the one that will have the least environmental impact.

My cycle assessment — two wheels, a bell, an uncomfortable seat...

Don't get your bike-cycle and life-cycle assessments confused. Life-cycle assessments are the ones you'll need.

Q1   For the example above, suggest four further things (that aren't outlined in the table) that the company should consider when forming a life-cycle assessment for the cars.   [4 marks]

Recycling Materials

Recycling's a hot topic. We don't have an infinite amount of materials, e.g. metals, to keep on making things from, so recycling's really important to make sure we don't run out of lots of important raw materials.

Extracting Raw Materials Requires Energy

1) Extracting raw materials can take large amounts of energy, lots of which comes from burning fossil fuels.

2) Fossil fuels are running out so it's important to conserve them. Not only this, but burning them contributes to acid rain and climate change (see pages 98-99).

3) Recycling materials often only uses a small fraction of the energy needed to extract and refine the material from scratch.

4) Energy doesn't come cheap, so recycling saves money too.

5) As there's a finite amount of many raw materials, e.g. metals, on Earth, recycling conserves these resources.

6) Recycling metal cuts down on the amount of rubbish that gets sent to landfill. Landfill takes up space and pollutes the surroundings.

Example: Recycling Aluminium

1) If you didn't recycle aluminium, you'd have to mine more aluminium ore — 4 tonnes for every 1 tonne of aluminium you need. But mining makes a mess of the landscape (and these mines are often in rainforests). The ore then needs to be transported, and the aluminium extracted (which uses loads of electricity). And don't forget the cost of sending your used aluminium to landfill.

2) So it's a complex calculation, but for every 1 kg of aluminium cans you recycle, you save:

- 95% or so of the energy needed to mine and extract 'fresh' aluminium,

- 4 kg of aluminium ore,

- a lot of waste.

In fact, aluminium's about the most cost-effective metal to recycle.

Sometimes Recycling isn't Straightforward

1) Recycling isn't an energy-free process. You need energy to reprocess the materials into new forms.

2) Often, items will need sorting to separate out different materials. Glass, for example, sometimes needs to be sorted into different colours, and different plastics need to be separated too.

Alloys (see page 78) can be difficult to sort for recycling as they're chemical mixtures.

3) Weighing up whether recycling a material is better than just disposing of it and starting from scratch, therefore requires you to compare how much energy is used for both these different processes.

4) Generally, you want to go for the option which has the lowest energy cost, but you also need to think about the consequences of putting materials in landfill, and whether the material you're considering recycling comes from a non-renewable or a renewable source.

5) You can also only recycle materials a finite number of times. Often, the recycled material is a lower quality than the original one, so has to be used differently. For example, paper can only usually be recycled a few times before it becomes useless. Recycled paper is often only used for toilet paper or cardboard, rather than high-quality printing paper.

My old robot friend died yesterday — may he rust in peace...

Cracking jokes like the ones you find in this book grow on trees you know. So to save trees and reduce the environmental costs of this book, I thought I'd recycle that hilarious pun from page 79. Aren't I good?

Q1   Material X is a metal. To recycle material X you need 110% of the energy used to extract and refine it. Explain why it might still be better to recycle material X than dispose of it in landfill.   [2 marks]

Types of Materials

The <u>properties</u> of materials are all to do with the <u>bonding</u> in them. Look back at Topic C2 for more about different types of bonding and how this affects something's properties. Now, more on properties. Lucky you.

There are Lots of Different Types of Polymer

Polymerisation reactions involving <u>different monomers</u> can be used to make a <u>wide range</u> of polymers. Different polymers have different <u>physical properties</u> — some are <u>stronger</u>, <u>stretchier</u>, more <u>easily moulded</u>, and so on. These physical properties make them suited for <u>different uses</u>. Here are just a few:

<u>Strong, rigid</u> polymers such as <u>high-density polyethene</u> are used to make water pipes.
<u>Light, stretchy</u> polymers such as <u>low-density polyethene</u> are used for plastic bags and squeezy bottles.
<u>Polystyrene foam</u> is used in <u>packaging</u> to protect breakable things, and as a <u>thermal insulator</u>.
<u>Heat-resistant</u> polymers such as <u>melamine</u> resin and <u>polypropene</u> are used to make <u>plastic kettles</u>.

See pages 90-91 for more on polymers.

Ceramics are Stiff but Brittle

<u>Ceramics</u> are made by baking substances, such as clay, to produce a <u>brittle</u>, <u>stiff</u> material. Examples of ceramics include <u>glass</u>, <u>porcelain</u> and <u>bone china</u>.

Ceramics tend to have either giant covalent structures (see page 21) or giant ionic structures (see page 19).

Pottery and Bricks are Made from Clay

1) <u>Clay</u> is a mineral formed from <u>weathered</u> and <u>decomposed rock</u>. It's <u>soft</u> when it's <u>dug up</u> out of the ground, which makes it <u>easy to mould</u> into different shapes required for pottery or bricks.

2) It can be <u>hardened</u> by firing at very <u>high temperatures</u>. This makes it <u>ideal</u> as a <u>building</u> material — clay bricks can <u>withstand</u> the <u>weight</u> of lots <u>more bricks</u> on top of them.

Most Glass is Made by Melting Limestone, Sand and Soda

1) <u>Glass</u> is generally <u>transparent</u> and <u>strong</u>, can be <u>moulded</u> when hot and can be <u>brittle</u> when thin.

2) The majority of glass made is <u>soda-lime glass</u> which is made by heating <u>limestone</u>, <u>sand</u> and <u>sodium carbonate</u> (soda) until they melt. When the mixture cools it comes out as <u>glass</u>.

Composites are Made of Different Materials

Composites are made of one material (the reinforcement) <u>embedded</u> in another (the matrix/binder). The <u>properties</u> of a composite depend on the properties of the materials it is <u>made from</u>. For example:

polymer matrix
glass fibres

1) <u>Fibreglass</u> consists of <u>fibres</u> of glass embedded in a <u>matrix</u> made of a polymer. It has a <u>low density</u> (like the polymer matrix) but is <u>very strong</u> (like glass). These properties mean fibreglass is used for things like <u>skis</u> and <u>boats</u>.

2) <u>Concrete</u> is made from <u>aggregate</u> (a mixture of sand and gravel) embedded in <u>cement</u>. It has a high <u>compressive strength</u> (it doesn't break if it's squashed). This makes it ideal for use as a <u>building material</u>, e.g. in skate parks.

3) <u>KEVLAR®-based composites</u> are made from <u>KEVLAR®</u> (a man-made polymer that's really <u>strong</u>) embedded in another material. KEVLAR® is often used as an ingredient in composite materials, as it adds a lot of <u>strength</u> without adding much <u>weight</u>. It's used in <u>cycling helmets</u>, <u>tennis racquets</u> and <u>ropes</u>.

4) Recently, <u>carbon fibre</u> composites have been made using carbon atoms bonded together to make carbon fibres or carbon <u>nanotubes</u> (see page 22) held together in a polymer resin matrix. These polymers are expensive to make but are very <u>strong</u> and <u>light</u> making them ideal for use in aerospace and sports car manufacturing.

People in soda-lime glass houses shouldn't throw heated objects...

It's amazing what they can do with composites these days. I reckon one might even end up running the country one day. Even if they don't become our inanimate leaders, they have definitely changed the modern world.

Q1   Name two types of ceramics.   [1 mark]

Topic C6 — Global Challenges

Materials and their Uses

It's all very well making a material but it needs to be <u>fit for purpose</u>. You need to be able to understand <u>why</u> a certain material is used and <u>not</u> another material. For example, a fire guard made of iron instead of chocolate.

Different Materials are Suited to Different Jobs

What materials are used for depends on their <u>properties</u>. In the <u>exam</u> they might ask you to <u>interpret information</u> about the properties of materials and <u>assess</u> the <u>suitability</u> of these materials for different purposes.

You should know all about the bonding in metals (see page 24) and polymers (see page 23).

<u>Polymers</u> are really adaptable — for example, they're often <u>flexible</u>, so they can be bent without breaking, and can be <u>easily moulded</u> into almost any shape. They're often <u>cheaper</u> than most other materials, and they also tend to be <u>less dense</u> than most metals or ceramics, so they're often used when designing products that need to have a low mass. They're also <u>thermal</u> and <u>electrical insulators</u>. But, polymers can <u>degrade</u> and <u>break down</u> over time, so polymer products don't always last as long as those made from other materials.

<u>Ceramics</u>, like polymers, are <u>insulators</u> of heat and electricity. They're much more <u>brittle</u> and <u>stiff</u> than most other materials, but they're also <u>strong</u> and <u>hard wearing</u>. They don't <u>degrade</u> or <u>corrode</u> like other materials can, so they last a lot longer — that's why we still use glass in windows instead of clear plastic.

<u>Metals</u> are <u>good conductors</u> of <u>heat</u> and <u>electricity</u> — which can be an advantage or a disadvantage, depending on what the material is needed for. They're <u>malleable</u>, so like polymers they can be formed into a variety of shapes. Some metals corrode easily, but products made from <u>corrosion resistant</u> metals can last for a very long time. Metals are usually <u>less brittle</u> than either ceramics or polymers, so they're likely to <u>deform</u> but stay in one piece where other materials may <u>shatter</u>.

<u>Composites</u> have different properties depending on the <u>matrix/binder</u> and the <u>reinforcement</u>. The combination of <u>component materials</u> used can be altered, so composites can be designed to have specific properties for a <u>specific purpose</u>. The main <u>disadvantage</u> of composites is that they tend to be much more <u>expensive</u> to produce than other materials.

You Need to Be Able to Interpret Information about Materials

You can <u>use information</u> about the properties of materials and <u>assess</u> their <u>suitability</u> for different uses.

EXAMPLE: A company is investigating the best material to make a fencing sword. The sword needs to be strong and lightweight, and is intended to be sold mainly to beginners to the sport of fencing. Using the data in the table, suggest which material from the table the company should use.

Material	Density (g/cm³)	Strength (MPa)	Cost
Steel	7.8	780	Low
Polypropylene	0.94	48	Low
Copper	8.9	220	Medium
Carbon Fibre	1.5	4100	High

Polypropylene can be ruled out — it's cheap and light but a lot weaker than all the other options.

Copper's heavier, weaker and more expensive than steel, so it can't be the best option.

Carbon fibre is really strong and light, but it's also expensive.
This is a sword for beginners, so the price should be kept down.

Steel swords will have a fairly high strength relative to their weight and would be cheap to make. So **steel** is the best material for the job.

As well as making sure a product is <u>fit for its purpose</u>, <u>life-cycle assessment data</u> (see page 84) is also used to work out how <u>environmentally friendly</u> manufacturing, using and disposing of a product is.

Compost-sites — piles of old vegetables embedded in muck...

So, you can't use any old material for any old job. My steel pillow and my glass duvet taught me that.

Q1   Look at the table in the example above. Given that polypropylene and carbon fibre are poor thermal conductors, steel is a good thermal conductor and copper is a very good thermal conductor, which of the four materials would you use to make an insulating coffee flask? Explain your answer.   [3 marks]

Alkanes and Alkenes

Alkanes and alkenes are dead useful. And all there is to them is some hydrogen and some carbon. Wonderful.

Alkanes are Saturated Hydrocarbons

1) A homologous series is a group of chemicals that have similar chemical structures.

2) Alkanes are a homologous series of hydrocarbons — they contain just carbon and hydrogen atoms.

3) Different alkanes have chains of different lengths. These are the first four alkanes:

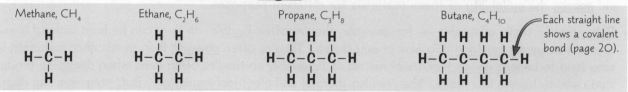

Each straight line shows a covalent bond (page 20).

4) The diagrams above show that all the atoms have formed bonds with as many other atoms as they can — this means they're saturated.

Carbon atoms tend to make four bonds, but hydrogen atoms can only make one.

5) Alkanes all have the general formula C_nH_{2n+2}. So if an alkane has 5 carbons, it's got to have $(2 \times 5) + 2 = 12$ hydrogens.

6) Alkanes (and other hydrocarbons) take part in combustion reactions. During a complete combustion reaction, they burn in oxygen to form carbon dioxide and water.

$$C_2H_6 + 3\frac{1}{2}O_2 \rightarrow 2CO_2 + 3H_2O$$
ethane + oxygen → carbon dioxide + water

$$C_2H_6 + 2\frac{1}{2}O_2 \rightarrow 2CO + 3H_2O$$
ethane + oxygen → carbon monoxide + water

7) Incomplete combustion happens in a limited supply of oxygen. During incomplete combustion, carbon monoxide is produced. Carbon, in the form of soot, can also be given out.

These two combustion reactions can happen at the same time, giving a mixture of combustion products.

Alkenes Have a C=C Double Bond

1) Alkenes are a homologous series of hydrocarbons with at least one carbon-carbon double bond.

2) They are known as unsaturated because they can make more bonds — the double bond can open up, allowing the two carbon atoms to bond with other atoms.

3) The first four alkenes are ethene, propene, butene and pentene (see below).

4) Alkenes have the general formula C_nH_{2n} — they have twice as many hydrogens as carbons.

In longer chains, the double bond can go at the end of the chain or in the middle.

5) You can test for an alkene using bromine water. When added to bromine water, an alkene will decolourise the bromine water, turning it from orange to colourless. This is because the double bond can open up and form bonds with the bromine.

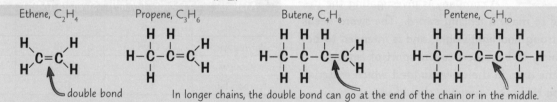

Example:

colourless   orange   colourless

Alkanes, don't react with bromine water as they don't contain double bonds.

orange bromine water + alkene

SHAKE

solution goes colourless

6) Alkenes can also be reacted with hydrogen in a process called hydrogenation. The hydrogen reacts with the double-bonded carbons and adds across the double bond.

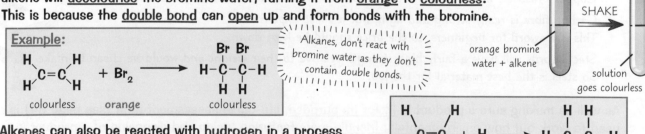

Britain's weather is a bit like alkanes — saturated...

Don't get alkanes and alkenes confused. That double bond makes a lot of difference.

Q1   Write a balanced chemical equation to show the complete combustion of butane.   [1 mark]

Topic C6 — Global Challenges

Alcohols

This page is about different types of <u>alcohols</u> — and that's not just beer, wine and other pub favourites.
But there may be some useful chemistry knowledge in here to help with that science round at the pub quiz...

Alcohols Have an '-OH' Functional Group and End in '-ol'

1) The <u>general formula</u> of an alcohol is $C_nH_{2n+1}OH$. So an alcohol with 2 carbons has the formula C_2H_5OH.

2) All alcohols contain an <u>-OH functional group</u>. Here are the <u>first four</u> alcohols in the homologous series:

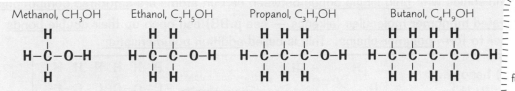

Methanol, CH_3OH Ethanol, C_2H_5OH Propanol, C_3H_7OH Butanol, C_4H_9OH

A functional group's a group of atoms that determines how a molecule reacts. Members of a homologous series all contain the same functional group (e.g. alcohols all contain -OH and alkenes contain C=C).

3) The basic <u>naming</u> system is the same as for alkanes
— but replace the final '<u>-e</u>' with '<u>-ol</u>'.

4) Don't write CH_4O instead of CH_3OH — it doesn't show the <u>functional -OH group</u>.

5) It is possible to get alcohols where the -OH group is attached to different carbon atoms in the carbon chain, or alcohols with more than one -OH group (like the ones that form condensation polymers on page 91).

Alcohols Can Be Oxidised to Form Carboxylic Acids

1) When something's <u>oxidised</u>, it gains oxygen.

2) Alcohols can be oxidised to form <u>carboxylic acids</u>. You need an oxidising agent, such as <u>potassium manganate(VII)</u>, for this.

Oxidation can also describe the loss of electrons (see page 47).

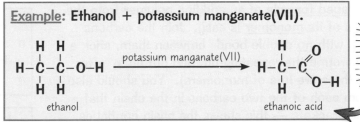

<u>Example:</u> Ethanol + potassium manganate(VII).

ethanol →(potassium manganate(VII))→ ethanoic acid

Alcohols can only form carboxylic acids in this way if the -OH group is attached to a carbon that's only attached to one carbon itself.

*This reaction's accompanied by a colour change — the reaction mixture goes from **purple** to colourless.*

3) The basic <u>naming</u> system for carboxylic acids is the same as for alkanes — but replace the final '<u>-e</u>' with '<u>-oic acid</u>'.

4) Carboxylic acids are another homologous series of molecules. They have the <u>general formula</u> $C_{n-1}H_{2n-1}COOH$ and they have a <u>-COOH functional group</u>.

5) Here are the <u>first four carboxylic acids</u> in the homologous series. They can each be formed by oxidising the alcohol which contains the same <u>total number of carbons</u> (i.e. methanol is oxidised to methanoic acid, ethanol is oxidised to ethanoic acid, and so on).

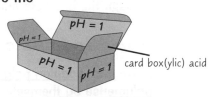

card box(ylic) acid

Methanoic acid, HCOOH   Ethanoic acid, CH_3COOH Propanoic acid, C_2H_5COOH Butanoic acid, C_3H_7COOH

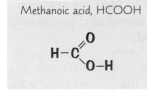
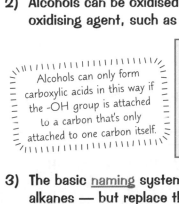
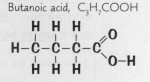

At every firework display, there's an -OH group and an -AH group...

Two more homologous series for you. Let's see if you've got them sussed with some practice questions.

Q1   What is the name given to the alcohol with the formula C_3H_7OH?   [1 mark]

Q2   A student reacts an unknown alcohol with potassium manganate(VII) and forms butanoic acid.
What's the name of the alcohol that the student must have started with?   [1 mark]

Addition Polymerisation

Polymers are made by joining lots of <u>little molecules</u> together in <u>long chains</u>. Magic.

Addition Polymers are Made From Unsaturated Monomers

1) <u>Polymers</u> are made by joining up lots of small molecules called <u>monomers</u>.
   The monomers that make up <u>addition polymers</u> have a <u>double covalent bond</u>.

2) Molecules with <u>at least one double covalent bond</u> between <u>carbon atoms</u> are called <u>unsaturated compounds</u>. Molecules with <u>only single bonds</u> between carbon atoms are <u>saturated compounds</u>.

3) Lots of <u>unsaturated monomer molecules</u> (<u>alkenes</u> — see p.88) can open up their <u>double bonds</u> and join together to form <u>polymer chains</u>. This is called <u>addition polymerisation</u>.

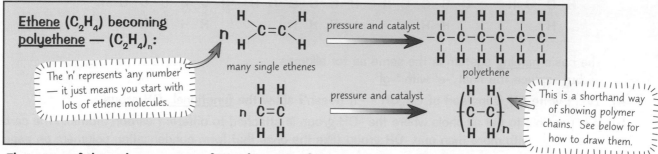

Ethene (C_2H_4) becoming polyethene — $(C_2H_4)_n$:

The 'n' represents 'any number' — it just means you start with lots of ethene molecules.

many single ethenes → polyethene

This is a shorthand way of showing polymer chains. See below for how to draw them.

4) The <u>name</u> of the polymer comes from the <u>type of monomer</u> it's made from — you just stick the word "<u>poly</u>" in front of it. So <u>propene</u> becomes <u>polypropene</u>, etc.

5) To get the <u>formula</u> of the polymer, you just put the formula of the <u>monomer</u> in brackets and put a little 'n' after it. So C_3H_6 becomes $(C_3H_6)_n$.

You Can Draw the Repeat Unit of a Polymer

1) Drawing the <u>displayed formula</u> of an addition polymer from the displayed formula of its <u>monomer</u> is easy. Join the carbons together in a <u>row</u> with <u>no</u> double bonds between them, stick a pair of <u>brackets</u> around the repeating bit, and put an '<u>n</u>' after it (to show that there are lots of monomers). You should also draw a bond from each of the two carbons in the chain that pass through the brackets — this shows the chain continues.

2) To get from the <u>displayed formula</u> of the <u>polymer</u> to the displayed formula of the <u>monomer</u>, just do the reverse. Draw out the <u>repeating bit</u> of the polymer, get rid of the two bonds going out through the brackets and put a <u>double bond</u> between the <u>carbons</u>.

Chloroethene → Polychloroethene

Polypropene → Propene

You Need an Initiator to Make Addition Polymers in the Lab

1) Making up <u>addition polymers</u> can be quite tricky. Alkenes <u>don't</u> just spontaneously <u>polymerise by themselves</u>. You have to add a chemical called an <u>initiator</u> to get things going.

2) Once you've added your initiator to your alkene monomers, you may have to <u>heat</u> the reaction mixture too. Because making addition polymers often involves <u>flammable</u> chemicals, you should use a <u>water bath</u>, rather than a Bunsen burner, to heat your reaction vessel.

Example: To make polystyrene (a common plastic used in packaging), you need to heat phenylethene (your monomer) in a water bath with the initiator (in this case a chemical called di(dodecanoyl) peroxide).

This reaction should be carried out in a fume hood. You should also wear safety goggles and a lab coat.

A pretty polymer — a parrot that just keeps going on...

Make sure you're completely sure about monomers, and how polymers are made.

Q1 Draw the repeat unit for the polymer formed when monomers of 1,2-dichloroethene (shown on the right) are reacted together.

1,2-dichloroethene [1 mark]

Condensation Polymerisation

Condensation polymers? Concentration polymers more like. They're trickier than their addition polymer cousins.

Polymers can be Made by Condensation Polymerisation

1) Condensation polymerisation usually involves two different types of monomer.

2) The monomers react together and bonds form between them, making polymer chains.

3) Each monomer has to contain at least two functional groups, one on each end of the molecule.

4) Each functional group can react with the functional group of another monomer, creating long chains of alternating monomers. For each new bond that forms, a small molecule (e.g. water) is lost.

Polyesters and Polyamides are Condensation Polymers

1) Polyesters form when carboxylic acid monomers and alcohol monomers react together.

The blocks represent the rest of each molecule.

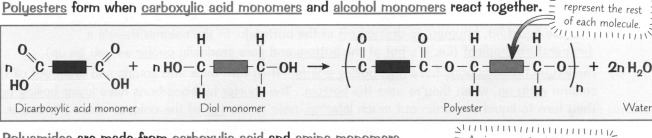

Dicarboxylic acid monomer   Diol monomer   Polyester   Water

2) Polyamides are made from carboxylic acid and amine monomers.

Amines contain -NH_2 groups.

Dicarboxylic acid monomer   Diamine monomer   Polyamide   Water

Nylon-6,6 is a Condensation Polymer that can be Made in the Lab

1) To make nylon-6,6, mix 1,6-diaminohexane in water in one beaker. In a separate beaker, mix 1,6-hexanedioyl dichloride in an organic solvent.

2) Pour one solution on top of the other. If you're careful not to mix the solutions, you get two distinct layers. Nylon is formed where these two layers meet.

3) You can extract this layer carefully by slowly lifting it out of the beaker with tweezers and collecting it by wrapping the nylon, which forms as a thread, around a rod.

nylon thread

There are Many Important Naturally Occurring Polymers

1) DNA is a complex molecule that contains genetic information.

2) It contains two strands made of nucleotide monomers that bond together in a polymerisation reaction.

3) There are four different nucleotide monomers in DNA — adenosine monophosphate (A), guanosine monophosphate (G), cytidine monophosphate (C) and thymidine monophosphate (T).

1) Carbohydrates are molecules containing carbon, oxygen and hydrogen, used by living things to produce energy.

2) Starch and cellulose are large, complex carbohydrates, which are made up of many smaller units of carbohydrates, known as sugars, joined together in a long chain.

1) Amino acids form polymers known as proteins via condensation polymerisation.

2) Proteins have many important uses in the human body, e.g. in enzymes (see page 72).

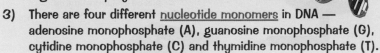

Amino acid monomer   Protein

Proteins are polyamides.

Revision's like polymers — it's all about stringing facts together...

DNA, polyesters, polyamides. Gosh, what a lot to learn. Best get some practice in with this question.

Q1   What two types of monomers react together to form polyesters?   [2 marks]

Crude Oil

Fossil fuels like coal, oil and gas are called non-renewable fuels as they take so long to make that they're being used up much faster than they're being formed. They're finite resources — one day they'll run out.

Crude Oil is Separated into Different Hydrocarbon Fractions

1) Crude oil is formed from the buried remains of plants and animals — it's a fossil fuel. Over millions of years, with high temperature and pressure, the remains turn to crude oil, which can be drilled up.

2) Crude oil is a mixture of lots of different hydrocarbons. It's mainly made up of fractions with the general formula C_nH_{2n+2}, i.e. alkanes.

3) Crude oil is our main source of hydrocarbons and is used as a raw material (or feedstock) to create lots of petrochemicals, for example, petrol or natural gas.

4) The different compounds in crude oil are separated by fractional distillation. The oil is heated until most of it has turned into gas. The gases enter a fractionating column (and the liquid bit, bitumen, is drained off at the bottom). In the column there's a temperature gradient (i.e. it's hot at the bottom and gets gradually cooler as you go up).

5) The longer hydrocarbons have high boiling points. They turn back into liquids and drain out of the column early on, when they're near the bottom. The shorter hydrocarbons have lower boiling points. They turn to liquid and drain out much later on, near to the top of the column where it's cooler.

6) You end up with the crude oil mixture separated out into different fractions. Each fraction contains a mixture of hydrocarbons, mostly alkanes (see page 88) with similar boiling points.

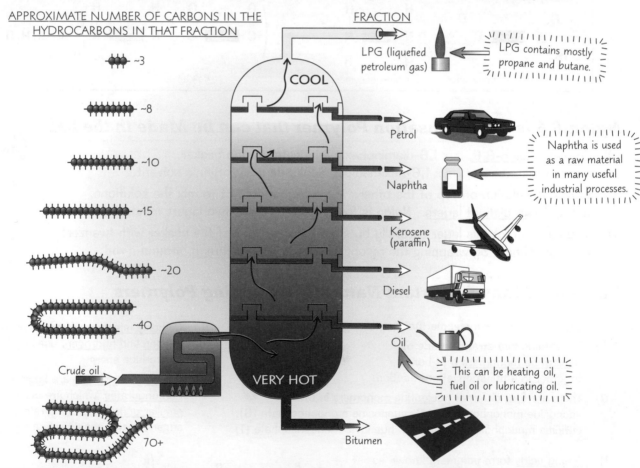

APPROXIMATE NUMBER OF CARBONS IN THE HYDROCARBONS IN THAT FRACTION

FRACTION

~3

~8

~10

~15

~20

~40

Crude oil

70+

COOL

VERY HOT

LPG (liquefied petroleum gas)

Petrol

Naphtha

Kerosene (paraffin)

Diesel

Oil

Bitumen

LPG contains mostly propane and butane.

Naphtha is used as a raw material in many useful industrial processes.

This can be heating oil, fuel oil or lubricating oil.

How much petrol is there in crude oil? Just a fraction...

Crude oil is pretty useful, so it's worth having a good read of this page to make sure you know all about it. You need to know it all for your exams, even the names of all the fractions. Yep, all of them.

Q1 Name the fractions in crude oil, in order of chain length, starting with the shortest, that are produced when crude oil is separated using fractional distillation. [5 marks]

Q2 What are the main components of LPG (liquid petroleum gas)? [1 mark]

Hydrocarbons

Fractional distillation (see last page) relies on the fact the different hydrocarbons have different boiling points. Time to find out why they do, and a bit more about crude oil besides. You lucky thing.

Crude Oil Separates Because of Different Intermolecular Forces

1) There are two important types of bond in crude oil:
   a) The strong covalent bonds between the atoms within each hydrocarbon molecule.
   b) The intermolecular forces of attraction between different hydrocarbon molecules in the mixture.

2) When the crude oil mixture is heated, the molecules are supplied with extra energy.

3) This makes the molecules move about more. Eventually a molecule might have enough energy to overcome the intermolecular forces that keep it with the other molecules. It can now go whizzing off as a gas.

4) The covalent bonds holding each molecule together are much stronger than the intermolecular forces, so they don't break. That's why you don't end up with lots of little molecules.

5) The intermolecular forces of attraction break a lot more easily in small molecules than they do in bigger molecules. That's because they are much stronger between big molecules than they are between small molecules.

6) It makes sense if you think about it — even if a big molecule can overcome the forces attracting it to another molecule at a few points along its length, it's still got lots of other places where the force is still strong enough to hold it in place.

7) That's why big molecules have higher boiling points than small molecules do.

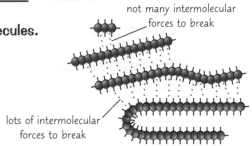

not many intermolecular forces to break

lots of intermolecular forces to break

Crude Oil Provides Important Fuels for Modern Life

1) Crude oil provides the energy needed to do lots of vital things — generating electricity, heating homes...

2) Oil provides the fuel for most modern transport — cars, trains, planes, the lot. It also provides the raw materials needed to make various chemicals, including plastics.

3) As Earth's population increases, and as countries like India and China become more developed, more fossil fuels are burned to provide electricity — both for increased home use and to run manufacturing industries.

But It Will Run Out Eventually... Eeek

1) Crude oil supplies are limited and non-renewable.

2) New reserves are sometimes found, and new technology means we can get to oil that was once too difficult to extract. But one day we'll just run out.

3) However long the oil lasts, it's a good idea to start thinking about alternative energy sources now — like using nuclear or wind power to generate electricity, ethanol to power cars, and solar energy to heat water. These alternatives aren't without their own problems, but we need them to be ready when the oil runs out.

4) Some people think we should stop using oil for fuel (where we have alternatives) and keep it for making plastics and other chemicals. This could lead to conflict for resources between the fuel and chemical industries.

I'd make a joke about oil, but it's too crude for a family product...

Crude oil's dead useful, but burning it isn't without it's problems though. Not only will it run out eventually, but burning crude oil churns loads of CO_2 into the air, which has its own issues (see pages 97-98).

Q1   Two straight-chain alkanes, A and B, have the chemical formulas C_5H_{12} and $C_{50}H_{102}$ respectively. Explain which alkane, A or B, you would expect to have a higher boiling point.   [2 marks]

Q2   Give three ways in which we use products derived from crude oil.   [3 marks]

Cracking

Crude oil fractions from fractional distillation are split into <u>smaller molecules</u> — this is called <u>cracking</u>. It's dead important — otherwise we might not have enough fuel for cars and planes and things.

Cracking is Splitting Up Long-Chain Hydrocarbons

1) <u>Cracking</u> turns long alkane molecules into <u>smaller</u> <u>alkane</u> and <u>alkene</u> molecules (which are much more <u>useful</u>).

2) It's a form of <u>thermal decomposition</u>, which is when one substance <u>breaks down</u> into at least two new ones when you <u>heat it</u>. This means breaking <u>strong covalent bonds</u>, so you need <u>lots of heat</u>. A <u>catalyst</u> is often added to speed things up.

3) A lot of the longer molecules produced from <u>fractional distillation</u> are <u>cracked</u> into smaller ones because there's <u>more demand</u> for products like <u>petrol</u> and <u>diesel</u> than for bitumen or lubricating oil.

4) Cracking also produces lots of <u>alkene</u> molecules, which can be used to make <u>polymers</u> (mostly plastics).

Cracking Involves Heat, Moderate Pressures and a Catalyst

1) <u>Vaporised hydrocarbons</u> are passed over <u>powdered catalyst</u> at about <u>400 °C – 700 °C</u> and <u>70 atm</u>.

2) <u>Aluminium oxide</u> is the <u>catalyst</u> used. The <u>long-chain</u> molecules <u>split apart</u> or 'crack' on the <u>surface</u> of the bits of catalyst.

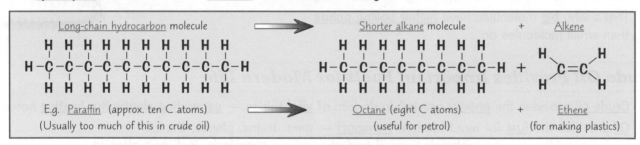

| <u>Long-chain hydrocarbon</u> molecule | <u>Shorter alkane</u> molecule | + | <u>Alkene</u> |

E.g. <u>Paraffin</u> (approx. ten C atoms) → <u>Octane</u> (eight C atoms) + <u>Ethene</u>
(Usually too much of this in crude oil) | (useful for petrol) | (for making plastics)

3) You can use the apparatus shown below to crack <u>liquid paraffin</u> in the lab:

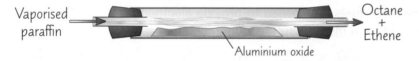

Vaporised paraffin → Aluminium oxide → Octane + Ethene

You'll probably get other products too — it all depends on what exactly is in your paraffin.

Cracking Helps Match Supply and Demand

The examiner might give you a <u>table</u> like the one below to show the <u>supply</u> and <u>demand</u> for various fractions obtained from crude oil. You could be asked which fraction is <u>more likely to be cracked</u> to provide us with petrol and diesel (demand for petrol and diesel is greater than the amount in crude oil).

Fraction	Approx % in crude oil	Approx % demand
LPG	2	4
Petrol and Naphtha	16	27
Kerosene	13	8
Diesel	19	23
Oil and Bitumen	50	38

OK, you could use the <u>kerosene fraction</u> to supply the extra <u>petrol</u> and the <u>oil and bitumen fraction</u> to supply the extra <u>diesel</u>.

Or you could crack the <u>oil and bitumen</u> to supply <u>both</u> the extra <u>petrol</u> and the extra <u>diesel</u>. This might be cleverer, as there's a lot more oil/bitumen.

Don't crack up — it's not that bad...

My incredible jokes crack me up all the time. Have you heard the one about the alkane and the chicken?

Q1   What conditions are used to crack hydrocarbons in industry?   [2 marks]

Q2   When a molecule of $C_{12}H_{26}$ is cracked under certain conditions, 2 molecules are made.
If one of the product molecules is C_3H_8, what is the other product?   [1 mark]

Fuel Cells

Fuel cells are great — they use hydrogen and oxygen to make electricity.

Hydrogen and Oxygen Give Out Energy When They React

1) Hydrogen and oxygen react to produce water.

2) The reaction between hydrogen and oxygen is exothermic — it releases energy. When the new bonds are formed the excess energy is given out in the form of heat.

See page 41 for more on reaction profiles.

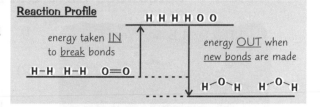

Reaction Profile

energy taken IN to break bonds

$H-H$ $H-H$ $O=O$

energy OUT when new bonds are made

$H-O-H$ $H-O-H$

Fuel Cells Use Fuel and Oxygen to Produce Electrical Energy

1) A fuel cell is an electrical cell that's supplied with a fuel and oxygen and uses energy from the reaction between them to produce electrical energy efficiently.

2) Chemical cells produce a potential difference across the cell, until all the reactants have been used up.

3) There are a few different types of fuel cells, using different fuels and different electrolytes.

4) For example, the hydrogen-oxygen fuel cell combines hydrogen and oxygen to release heat energy and nice clean water. That means there are no nasty pollutants to worry about.

Hydrogen-Oxygen Fuel Cells Involve a Redox Reaction

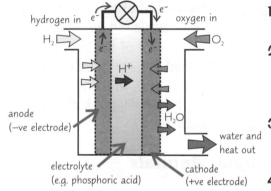

1) The electrolyte is often a solution of potassium hydroxide. The electrodes are often porous carbon with a catalyst.

2) Hydrogen goes into the anode compartment and oxygen goes into the cathode compartment.
Watch out — in electrolysis the anode is the positive electrode and the cathode is the negative one. When dealing with fuel cells, they're the other way round.

3) At the negative electrode, hydrogen loses electrons to produce H^+ ions. This is oxidation. $H_2 + \rightarrow 2H^+ + 2e^-$

4) H^+ ions in the electrolyte move to the positive electrode.

5) At the positive electrode, oxygen gains electrons from the electrode and reacts with H^+ ions (from the electrolyte) to make water. This is reduction. $O_2 + 4e^- + 2H_2O \rightarrow 4H_2O$

6) The electrons flow through an external circuit from the anode to the cathode — this is the electric current.

7) The overall reaction is hydrogen plus oxygen, which gives water.

hydrogen + oxygen → water
$2H_2 + O_2 \rightarrow 2H_2O$

There's reduction at the cathode and oxidation at the anode, so the whole thing is a redox reaction.

Fuel Cells Have Some Important Advantages

1) Fuel cells are great. Hydrogen fuel cells don't generate nasty pollutants when they produce energy, and they're also really efficient.

2) However it's not all roses. It would be really expensive to adapt our current technology to run off fuel cells. Also, hydrogen as a fuel is pretty difficult and expensive to extract and store.

A fuel cell — prison for disobedient petrolheads...

Just a handy hint from me — you may want to take a look back at page 47 for a reminder on reduction and oxidation.

Q1   Write out the overall reaction that occurs in a hydrogen-oxygen fuel cell.   [1 mark]

Q2   Give one advantage and one disadvantage of using fuel cells for energy.   [2 marks]

The Atmosphere

Scientists have looked at <u>evidence</u> from rocks, air bubbles in ice and fossils to see how our <u>atmosphere</u> has <u>changed</u> over many, many years. Here's one theory about how our atmosphere might have evolved.

Phase 1 — Volcanoes Gave Out Steam and CO_2

Holiday report: Not nice. Take strong walking boots and a coat.

1) The Earth's surface was originally <u>molten</u> for many millions of years. There was almost no atmosphere.

2) Eventually the Earth's surface cooled and a <u>thin crust</u> formed, but <u>volcanoes</u> kept erupting, releasing gases from <u>inside the Earth</u>. This '<u>degassing</u>' released mainly <u>carbon dioxide</u>, but also <u>steam</u>, <u>methane</u> and <u>ammonia</u>.

3) When things eventually settled down, the early atmosphere was <u>mostly CO_2</u> and water vapour (the water vapour later <u>condensed</u> to form the <u>oceans</u>). There was very little oxygen.

Phase 2 — Green Plants Evolved and Produced Oxygen

Holiday Report: A bit slimy underfoot. Take wellies and a lot of suncream.

1) A lot of the early CO_2 <u>dissolved</u> into the oceans.

2) <u>Nitrogen gas (N_2)</u> was then put into the atmosphere in two ways — it was formed by ammonia reacting with oxygen, and was released by denitrifying bacteria.

3) N_2 isn't very <u>reactive</u>. So the amount of N_2 in the atmosphere <u>increased</u>, because it was being <u>made</u> but not <u>broken down</u>.

4) Next, <u>green plants</u> evolved over most of the Earth. As they photosynthesised, they <u>removed CO_2</u> and <u>produced O_2</u>.

5) Thanks to the plants the amount of O_2 in the air gradually <u>built up</u> and much of the CO_2 eventually got <u>locked up</u> in <u>fossil fuels</u> and <u>sedimentary rocks</u>.

Phase 3 — Ozone Layer Allows Evolution of Complex Animals

1) The build-up of <u>oxygen</u> in the atmosphere <u>killed off</u> early organisms that couldn't tolerate it.

2) But it did allow the <u>evolution</u> of more <u>complex</u> organisms that <u>made use</u> of the oxygen.

3) The oxygen also created the <u>ozone layer</u> (O_3), which <u>blocked</u> harmful rays from the Sun and <u>enabled</u> even <u>more complex</u> organisms to evolve.

4) There is virtually <u>no CO_2</u> left now.

Holiday report: A nice place to be. Get there before the crowds ruin it.

Today's Atmosphere is Just Right for Us

The <u>present composition</u> of Earth's atmosphere is:

78% nitrogen and 21% oxygen ←

There are also noble gases (mainly argon) and varying amounts of water vapour. About 0.04% of the atmosphere is carbon dioxide.

I went to a restaurant on the moon — nice view, no atmosphere...

We can breathe easy knowing that our atmosphere has developed into a lovely oxygen rich one. Aaaahh.

Q1 The atmosphere of Earth originally contained little or no nitrogen gas.
Explain how and why the proportion of nitrogen gas in the atmosphere increased over time. [3 marks]

The Greenhouse Effect

The <u>greenhouse effect</u> isn't a bumper crop of tomatoes and a prize winning marrow...

Human Activity Affects the Composition of Air

1) The <u>human population is increasing</u>, so there are more people <u>respiring</u>, giving out <u>more carbon dioxide</u>.

2) More people means that <u>more energy</u> is needed for lighting, heating, cooking, transport and so on. People's <u>lifestyles</u> are changing too. More and more countries are becoming <u>industrialised</u> and <u>well-off</u>. This means the average <u>energy demand per person</u> is also increasing (since people have <u>more electrical gadgets</u>, more people have <u>cars</u> or <u>travel on planes</u>, etc.). This increased energy consumption comes mainly from the <u>burning of fossil fuels</u>, which releases <u>more CO_2</u>.

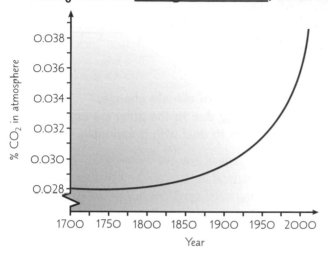

3) More people also means more land is needed to build <u>houses</u> and grow <u>food</u>. This space is often made by <u>chopping down trees</u> — this is called <u>deforestation</u>. But plants are the main things <u>taking carbon dioxide out of the atmosphere</u> (as they photosynthesise) — so fewer plants means less carbon dioxide is <u>taken out</u> of the atmosphere.

> So, as the consumption of fossil fuels increases, as does the concentration of CO_2 in the atmosphere.

4) The graph shows how CO_2 levels in the atmosphere have <u>risen</u> over the last <u>300</u> years.

The Greenhouse Effect Helps to Keep the Earth Warm

1) The <u>Sun</u> gives out <u>electromagnetic radiation</u>.

2) <u>Some</u> electromagnetic radiation, at most wavelengths, <u>passes through</u> the atmosphere.

3) The electromagnetic radiation with short wavelengths is <u>absorbed</u> by the Earth — <u>warming</u> our planet.

> The greenhouse effect is very important — it's what keeps the Earth warm enough for us to live on.

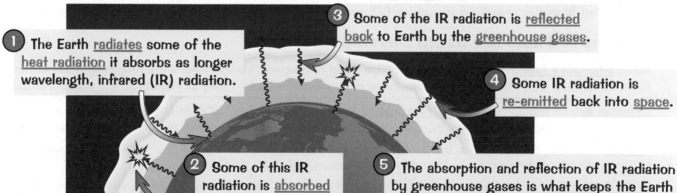

1 The Earth <u>radiates</u> some of the <u>heat radiation</u> it absorbs as longer wavelength, infrared (IR) radiation.

2 Some of this IR radiation is <u>absorbed</u> by <u>greenhouse gases</u>.

3 Some of the IR radiation is <u>reflected back</u> to Earth by the <u>greenhouse gases</u>.

4 Some IR radiation is <u>re-emitted</u> back into <u>space</u>.

5 The absorption and reflection of IR radiation by greenhouse gases is what keeps the Earth <u>warm</u>. It's called the <u>greenhouse effect</u>.

<u>Greenhouse gases</u> are the <u>gases</u> in the atmosphere that can <u>absorb and reflect heat radiation</u>. They're only present in <u>small amounts</u>. <u>Carbon dioxide</u>, <u>water vapour</u> and <u>methane</u> are three <u>greenhouse gases</u>.

4) If the concentration of greenhouse gases in the atmosphere increases, you get an <u>enhanced greenhouse effect</u>. This is where <u>more heat radiation</u> from the earth is absorbed and less is re-emitted back into space. This causes the atmosphere to <u>heat up</u> (see next page).

The White House effect — heated political debates...

Is all this hot air isn't making you a bit hot and bothered? If so, here are some questions to cheer you up.

Q1 Outline how the greenhouse effect works to keep our planet warm. [3 marks]

Q2 Name three greenhouse gases. [3 marks]

Global Warming

Is it me, or is it getting <u>hot</u> in here...?

Increasing Greenhouse Gases Causes Climate Change

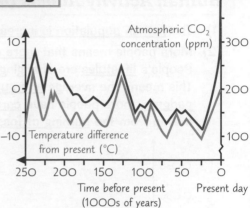

Atmospheric CO_2 concentration (ppm)

Temperature difference from present (°C)

Time before present (1000s of years)

Present day

1) You saw on the last page that the level of <u>carbon dioxide</u> in the atmosphere is <u>increasing</u>, but that's not the whole story...

2) The greenhouse gas methane is also causing problems. The concentration of <u>methane</u> has risen lots in recent years. Though it's currently only present in <u>tiny amounts</u> in our atmosphere, the increasing concentration of methane is an issue as it's a super effective <u>greenhouse gas</u>.

3) There's a <u>scientific consensus</u> that extra greenhouse gases from <u>human activity</u> have caused the average <u>temperature</u> of the Earth to <u>increase</u>, due to the enhanced greenhouse effect — see previous page. This effect is known as global warming.

4) Global warming is a type of <u>climate change</u> and causes other types of climate change, e.g. changing rainfall patterns. It could also cause severe <u>flooding</u> due to the polar ice caps melting. It's a BIG problem that could affect the whole world, so we need to deal with it seriously.

> Most of the scientific community agree that global warming is <u>anthropogenic</u> (caused by humans). But some scientists believe that the current rises in global temperature are just <u>natural fluctuations</u> and that we don't have <u>enough data</u> to prove that global warming is caused by increasing CO_2 emissions or human activity.

We Can Try To Use Less Fossil Fuels

1) In order to prevent or <u>slow down climate change</u>, we need to <u>cut down</u> on the amount of greenhouse gases we're releasing into the atmosphere.

2) To <u>reduce carbon dioxide emissions</u>, we can try to limit our own use of fossil fuels. This could be doing things on a personal level, like <u>walking</u> or <u>cycling</u> instead of driving or <u>turning your central heating down</u>.

3) On a larger scale, the UK government has formed plans to encourage the public and industry to become more <u>energy efficient</u> and use more renewable energy. The government has also created financial incentives to reduce CO_2 emissions and increased research into new energy sources.

Alternative Fuels are Being Developed

Some <u>alternative fuels</u> have already been, or are being developed. Many of them are <u>renewable</u> fuels so, unlike fossil fuels, they won't run out. However, none of them are perfect — they all have <u>pros and cons</u>. For example:

> <u>Ethanol</u> can be produced from <u>plant material</u> so is known as a <u>biofuel</u>. It's made by <u>fermentation</u> of plants and is used to power <u>cars</u> in some places. It's often mixed with petrol to make a better fuel.
>
> <u>PROS:</u> The CO_2 released when it's burnt was taken in by the plant as it grew, so it's '<u>carbon neutral</u>'. The only other product is <u>water</u>.
>
> <u>CONS:</u> <u>Engines</u> need to be <u>converted</u> before they'll work with ethanol fuels. And ethanol fuel <u>isn't widely available</u>. There are worries that as demand for it increases farmers will switch from growing food crops to growing crops to make ethanol — this will <u>increase food prices</u>.

> <u>Biodiesel</u> is another type of <u>biofuel</u>. It can be produced from <u>vegetable oils</u> such as rapeseed oil and soybean oil. Biodiesel can be mixed with ordinary diesel fuel and used to run a <u>diesel engine</u>.
>
> <u>PROS:</u> Biodiesel is '<u>carbon neutral</u>'. <u>Engines don't</u> need to be <u>converted</u>. It produces much <u>less sulfur dioxide</u> and <u>other pollutants</u> than regular diesel or petrol.
>
> <u>CONS:</u> We <u>can't make enough</u> to completely replace diesel. It's <u>expensive</u> to make. It could <u>increase food prices</u> like using more ethanol could (see above).

> Another clean, alternative fuel is hydrogen gas. It can be used in hydrogen-oxygen fuel cells (page 95).

Give the climate some privacy — it's changing...

It's not all depressing news. There are steps we can take to cut our carbon dioxide emissions, so chin up.

Q1   What is global warming and how is it caused?   [2 marks]

Pollutants

You get loads of nasties like oxides of nitrogen, sulfur dioxide and carbon monoxide when you burn fossil fuels.

Acid Rain is Caused by Sulfur Dioxide and Oxides of Nitrogen

1) When fossil fuels are burned they release mostly CO_2 (a big cause of global warming).
2) But they also release other harmful gases — especially sulfur dioxide and various nitrogen oxides.
3) The sulfur dioxide (SO_2) comes from sulfur impurities in the fossil fuels.
4) The nitrogen oxides are created from a reaction between the nitrogen and oxygen in the air, caused by the heat of the burning. (This can happen in the internal combustion engines of cars.)
5) When these gases mix with clouds they form dilute sulfuric acid and dilute nitric acid.
6) This then falls as acid rain.
7) Power stations and internal combustion engines in cars are the main causes of acid rain.

Acid Rain Kills Fish, Trees and Statues

1) Acid rain causes lakes to become acidic and many plants and animals die as a result.
2) Acid rain kills trees and damages limestone buildings and ruins some stone statues. It also makes metal corrode.

Oxides of Nitrogen Also Cause Photochemical Smog

1) Photochemical smog is a type of air pollution caused by sunlight acting on oxides of nitrogen. These oxides combine with oxygen in the air to produce ozone (O_3).
2) Ozone can cause breathing difficulties, headaches and tiredness. (Don't confuse ground-level ozone with the useful ozone layer high up in the atmosphere.)

Carbon Monoxide is a Poisonous Gas

1) Carbon monoxide (CO) can stop your blood doing its proper job of carrying oxygen around the body.
2) A lack of oxygen in the blood can lead to fainting, a coma or even death.
3) Carbon monoxide is formed when carbon compounds are burnt without enough oxygen — this is incomplete combustion (see page 88 for more details).
4) One way carbon monoxide is produced is by incomplete combustion in petrol or diesel car engines.

Particulate Carbon is Caused by Incomplete Combustion

1) During incomplete combustion, small pieces of solids, called particulates, can be released into the atmosphere. These are mainly pieces of carbon, called particulate carbon.
2) If they escape into the atmosphere, which they often do, they just float around.
3) Eventually they fall back to the ground and deposit themselves as the horrible black dust we call soot.
4) Particulates also reduce air quality and can cause or worsen respiratory problems.

King Nitrogen Oxide had a long, prosperous acid reign...

Acid rain's bad news for sculptors, fish and trees alike. It's bad news for you too, as you need to know it...

Q1   How does acid rain form?   [2 marks]

Q2   Name two pollutants formed by incomplete combustion.   [2 marks]

Water Treatment

Water, water, everywhere... well, there is if you live in a submarine.

There are a Variety of Limited Water Resources in the UK

1) As well as for drinking, we need water for loads of domestic uses (mainly washing things).
2) Industrially, water is important as a cheap raw material, a coolant (especially in power stations) and a solvent. Between half and two thirds of all the fresh water used in the UK goes into industry.

In the UK, we get our water from:
- SURFACE WATER: lakes, rivers and reservoirs. In much of England and Wales, these sources start to run dry during the summer months.
- GROUNDWATER: aquifers (rocks that trap water underground). In parts of the south-east where surface water is very limited, as much as 70% of the domestic water supply comes from groundwater.

> You can also get clean water by treating wastewater (water that's been contaminated by a human process). This is preferable to disposing of the water, which can be polluting. How easy wastewater is to treat depends on the levels of contaminants in it.

All these resources are limited, depending on annual rainfall, and demand for water increases every year. Experts worry that, unless we limit our water use, by 2025 we might not have enough water to supply everybody's needs. So it's important to conserve water.

Water is Purified in Water Treatment Plants

How much purification the water needs depends on the source. Groundwater from aquifers is usually quite pure, but surface water needs a lot of treatment. Before we can use it, most water will be purified using the following processes:

1) Filtration — a wire mesh screens out large twigs etc., and then gravel and sand beds filter out any other solid bits.
2) Sedimentation — iron sulfate or aluminium sulfate is added to the water, which makes fine particles clump together and settle at the bottom.
3) Chlorination — chlorine gas is bubbled through to kill harmful bacteria and other microbes.

mesh

sand/gravel filtration

sedimentation

chlorination

Some soluble impurities that are dissolved in the water are not removed — because they can't be filtered out. These include minerals which cause water hardness and some harmful chemicals (see below).

Tap Water Can Still Contain Impurities

The water that comes out of our taps has to meet strict safety standards, but low levels of pollutants are still found. These pollutants come from various sources:

1) Nitrate residues from excess fertiliser 'run-off' into rivers and lakes. If too many nitrates get into drinking water it can cause serious health problems, especially for young babies. Nitrates prevent the blood from carrying oxygen properly.
2) Lead compounds from old lead pipes. Lead is very poisonous, particularly in children.
3) Pesticide residues from spraying pesticides too near to rivers and lakes.

> Water that is fit to drink can be called potable water.

You Can Get Fresh Water by Distilling Sea Water

1) In some very dry countries, e.g. Kuwait, sea water is distilled to produce drinking water.
2) Distillation needs loads of energy, so it's really expensive and not practical for producing large quantities of fresh water.

If water from the ground is groundwater, why isn't rain sky water?

My huge congratulations on finishing this topic. Now for a celebratory biscuit and some questions.

Q1   Outline how surface water is purified in a water treatment plant.   [3 marks]

Q2   How do nitrate residues get into tap water and why are they dangerous?   [2 marks]

Revision Questions for Topic C6

Topic C6 is a pretty hefty topic, but it's the last one, so that makes it a pretty good topic all round.
- Try these questions and tick off each one when you get it right.
- When you've done all the questions under a heading and are completely happy with it, tick it off.

Metals, Alloys and Corrosion (p.76-79) ☐

1) Write a balanced equation to show how copper is extracted from copper oxide using carbon. ☐
2) Using the reactivity series, how can you use it to tell which metals can be extracted from their ores using reduction with carbon? ☑
3) Give an advantage and a disadvantage of using bioleaching, rather than electrolysis, to extract metals. ☑
4) Name four metal alloys and give a use for each one. ☑
5) Give two ways that you could prevent a block of iron from rusting. ☑

Industrial Processes (p.80-85) ☑

6) Explain why the conditions used in the Haber Process are a compromise between rate and yield. ☑
7) Name three different fertilisers and describe how they're made. ☑
8) In the Contact process, how would using low pressures affect the yield of H_2SO_4? ☑
9) Name five things that you should consider when designing an industrial reaction. ☑
10) What is a life-cycle assessment? ☑
11) Give two benefits of recycling. ☑

Properties and Uses of Materials (p.86-87) ☑

12) Name three composites and outline their properties. ☑
13) Are metals thermal conductors or insulators? ☑

Organic Molecules (p.88-91) ☑

14) What is the general formula of an alkane? ☑
15) What would you get if you reacted an alcohol with potassium manganate(VII)? ☑
16) What colour change would you see if you reacted an alcohol with potassium manganate(VII)? ☑
17) What alkene monomers are used to make polyethene? ☑
18) Name three biologically important condensation polymers. ☑

Crude Oil and Alternative Fuels (p.92-95) ☑

19) Name three fractions of crude oil. ☑
20) Why do long hydrocarbons have higher boiling points than short-chain hydrocarbons? ☑
21) What happens to an alkane when it's cracked? ☑
22) Outline how a hydrogen-oxygen fuel cell works. ☑

The Atmosphere and Air Pollution (p.96-99) ☑

23) Describe how the composition of our atmosphere changed over the last 4.5 billion years. ☑
24) What causes the enhanced greenhouse effect? ☑
25) Give three ways that we can combat global warming. ☑
26) What is acid rain and why is it a problem? ☑

Water Treatment (p.100) ☑

27) Name three impurities that could be present in tap water and where they come from. ☑

Practical Techniques

- <u>Topic C7</u> covers <u>practical skills</u> you'll need to know about for your course (including 15% of your exams).
- You're required to do at least <u>8 core practicals</u> (experiments). These are covered in <u>Topics C1-C6</u> earlier in the book and they're <u>highlighted</u> with <u>practical stamps</u> like this one.
- The following pages of this topic cover some <u>extra bits and bobs</u> you need to know about practical work. First up, safety in the lab...

> **PRACTICAL**

Solids Should Be Measured Using a Balance

1) To weigh a solid, start by putting the <u>container</u> you're weighing your substance <u>into</u> on the <u>balance</u>.

2) Set the balance to exactly <u>zero</u> and then start weighing out your substance.

3) It's <u>no good</u> carefully weighing out your solid if it's not all transferred to your reaction vessel — the amount in the <u>reaction vessel</u> won't be the same as your measurement. Here are a couple of methods you can use to make sure that your measurement is accurate...

> - If you're <u>dissolving</u> a solid in a solvent to make a <u>solution</u>, you could <u>wash</u> any remaining solid into the new container using the <u>solvent</u>. This way you know that <u>all</u> the solid you weighed has been transferred.
> - You could set the balance to zero <u>before</u> you put your <u>weighing container</u> on the balance. Then <u>reweigh</u> the weighing container <u>after</u> you've transferred the solid. Use the <u>difference in mass</u> to work out <u>exactly</u> how much solid you added to your experiment.

Three Ways to Measure Liquids

There are a few methods you might use to measure the volume of a liquid. Whichever method you use, always read the volume from the <u>bottom of the meniscus</u> (the curved upper surface of the liquid) when it's at <u>eye level</u>.

Read volume from here — the bottom of the meniscus.

pipette filler

> <u>Pipettes</u> are long, narrow tubes that are used to suck up an <u>accurate</u> volume of liquid and <u>transfer</u> it to another container. A <u>pipette filler</u> attached to the end of the pipette is used so that you can <u>safely control</u> the amount of liquid you're drawing up. Pipettes are often <u>calibrated</u> to allow for the fact that the last drop of liquid stays in the pipette when the liquid is ejected. This reduces <u>transfer errors</u>.

If you only want a couple of drops of liquid, and don't need it to be accurately measured, you can use a dropping pipette to transfer it. For example, this is how you'd add a couple of drops of indicator into a mixture.

> <u>Burettes</u> measure from top to bottom (so when they're filled to the top of the scale, the scale reads zero). They have a tap at the bottom which you can use to release the liquid into another container (you can even release it drop by drop). To use a burette, take an <u>initial reading</u>, and once you've released as much liquid as you want, take a <u>final reading</u>. The <u>difference</u> between the readings tells you <u>how much</u> liquid you used.

Burettes are used a lot for titrations. There's loads more about titrations on page 64.

> <u>Measuring cylinders</u> are the most common way to measure out a liquid. They come in all different <u>sizes</u>. Make sure you choose one that's the right size for the measurement you want to make. It's no good using a huge 1000 cm³ cylinder to measure out 2 cm³ of a liquid — the graduations will be too big, and you'll end up with <u>massive errors</u>. It'd be much better to use one that measures up to 10 cm³.

Gas Syringes Measure Gas Volumes

Gases can be measured with a gas syringe. They should be measured at <u>room temperature and pressure</u> as the <u>volume</u> of a gas <u>changes</u> with temperature and pressure. You should also use a gas syringe that's the <u>right size</u> for the measurement you're making. Before you use the syringe, you should make sure it's completely sealed and that the plunger moves smoothly.

Practical Techniques

Measure Temperature Accurately

You can use a thermometer to measure the temperature of a substance:

1) Make sure the bulb of your thermometer is completely submerged in any mixture you're measuring.
2) If you're taking an initial reading, you should wait for the temperature to stabilise first.
3) Read your measurement off the scale on a thermometer at eye level to make sure it's correct.

You May Have to Measure the Time Taken for a Change

1) You should use a stopwatch to time experiments. These measure to the nearest 0.1 s so are accurate.
2) Always make sure you start and stop the stopwatch at exactly the right time. For example, if you're investigating the rate of an experiment, you should start timing at the exact moment you mix the reagents and start the reaction. If you're measuring the time taken for a precipitate to form, you should watch the reaction like a hawk so you can stop timing the moment it goes cloudy.

Measure pH to Find Out How Acidic or Alkaline a Solution Is

You need to be able to decide the best method for measuring pH, depending on what your experiment is.

1) Indicators are dyes that change colour depending on whether they're in an acid or an alkali. You use them by adding a couple of drops of the indicator to the solution you're interested in. They're useful for titration reactions, when you want to find the point at which a solution is neutralised.
2) Single indicators are one colour in acids and another colour in alkalis. Examples of single indicators include litmus (red in acids, blue in alkalis) and phenolphthalein (colourless in acids, pink in alkalis).
3) Universal indicator is a mixed indicator — it's made by mixing together several single indicators. This means it changes through a whole series of colours as you go along the pH scale (it doesn't show one sudden colour change). It's useful for estimating the pH of a solution based on its colour.
4) Indicators can be soaked into paper and this paper can be used to test pH. If you put a small amount of a solution onto some indicator paper, it will change colour depending on the pH of the solution. Indicator paper is useful if you don't want to change the colour of all of the substance, or if the substance is coloured. You can also hold a piece of damp indicator paper in a gas sample to test its pH.
5) pH probes are attached to pH meters which have a digital display that gives a numerical value for the pH of a solution. They're used to give an accurate value of pH.

There's loads more about pH on page 43.

Be Careful When You Handle or Mix Substances

1) There are lots of hazards in chemistry experiments, so before you start any experiment, you should read any safety precautions to do with your method or the chemicals you're using.
2) The substances used in chemical reactions are often hazardous. For example, they might catch fire easily (they're flammable), or they might irritate or burn your skin if you come into contact with them.
3) Whenever you're doing an experiment, you should wear a lab coat, safety goggles and gloves.
4) Always be careful that the chemicals you're using aren't flammable before you go lighting any Bunsen burners, and make sure you're working in an area that's well ventilated.
5) If you're doing an experiment that might produce nasty gases (such as chlorine), you should carry out the experiment in a fume hood so that the gas can't escape out into the room you're working in.
6) Never directly touch any chemicals (even if you're wearing gloves). Use a spatula to transfer solids between containers. Carefully pour liquids between different containers, using a funnel to avoid spillages.
7) Be careful when you're mixing chemicals, as a reaction might occur. If you're diluting a liquid, add the concentrated substance to the water (not the other way around) or the mixture could get very hot.

The Tempipettes and MacBurette — Shakespeare for chemists...

It's no good throwing chemicals around willy nilly and calling it an experiment. To make sure your results are reproducible, so can be trusted by other scientists, you have to make sure all your measurements are accurate.

Setting Up Equipment

Setting up the equipment for an experiment correctly is <u>just as important</u> as making accurate measurements.

To Collect Gases, the System Needs to be Sealed

1) There are times when you might want to <u>collect</u> the gas produced by a reaction. For example, to investigate the <u>rate</u> of reaction.

2) The most accurate way to measure the volume of a gas that's been produced is to collect it in a <u>gas syringe</u> (see page 102).

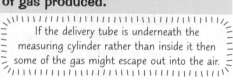

delivery tube

collected gas   gas syringe

reaction mixture

3) You could also collect it by <u>displacing water</u> from a measuring cylinder. Here's how you do it...

- Fill a <u>measuring cylinder</u> with <u>water</u>, and carefully place it <u>upside down</u> in a container of water. Record the <u>initial level</u> of the water in the measuring cylinder.

- Position a <u>delivery tube</u> coming <u>from</u> the reaction vessel so that it's <u>inside</u> the measuring cylinder, pointing upwards. Any gas that's produced will pass <u>through</u> the delivery tube and <u>into</u> the <u>measuring cylinder</u>. As the gas enters the measuring cylinder, the <u>water</u> is <u>pushed out</u>.

- Record the <u>level of water</u> in the measuring cylinder and use this value, along with your <u>initial value</u>, to calculate the <u>volume</u> of gas produced.

delivery tube

collected gas

measuring cylinder filled with water and upturned in a beaker of water

reaction mixture

4) When you're measuring a gas, your equipment has to be <u>sealed</u> or some gas could escape and your results wouldn't be <u>accurate</u>.

If the delivery tube is underneath the measuring cylinder rather than inside it then some of the gas might escape out into the air.

5) If just want to <u>collect</u> a sample to test (and don't need to measure a volume), you can collect it over water as above using a <u>test tube</u>. Once the test tube is full of gas, you can stopper it and store the gas for later.

There's more about electrolysis on pages 47-49.

You May Have to Identify the Products of Electrolysis

1) When you electrolyse an <u>aqueous solution</u>, the products of electrolysis will depend on how reactive the ions in the solution are compared to the H^+ and OH^- ions that come from water.

2) At the <u>cathode</u> you'll either get a <u>pure metal</u> coating the electrode or bubbles of <u>hydrogen gas</u>.

3) At the <u>anode</u>, you'll get bubbles of <u>oxygen gas</u> unless a <u>halide ion</u> is present, when you'll get the <u>halogen</u>.

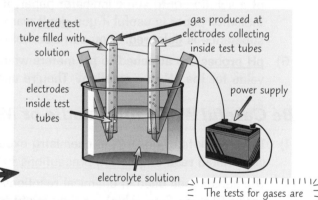

inverted test tube filled with solution

gas produced at electrodes collecting inside test tubes

electrodes inside test tubes

power supply

4) You may have to identify what's been made in an electrolysis experiment. To do this, you need to be able to <u>set up the equipment</u> correctly so that you can <u>collect</u> any gas that's produced. The easiest way to collect the gas is in a <u>test tube</u>.

5) Here's how to set up the equipment...

electrolyte solution

The tests for gases are described on page 58.

Make Sure You Can Draw Diagrams of Your Equipment

When you're writing out a <u>method</u> for your experiment, it's always a good idea to draw a <u>labelled diagram</u> showing how your apparatus will be <u>set up</u>. The easiest way to do this is to use a scientific drawing, where each piece of apparatus is drawn as if you're looking at its <u>cross-section</u>.
For example:

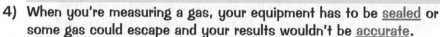

beaker   test tube   tripod   heat-proof mat   gauze   Bunsen burner

The pieces of glassware are drawn without tops so they aren't sealed. If you want to draw a closed system, remember to draw a bung in the top.

I set up my equipment — they had a blind date at the cinema...

Being a dab hand at setting up experiments won't just make your investigations more reliable. You might also be asked to comment on how an experiment's been set up in the exam. So best get learning. You'll thank me for it...

Heating Substances

Heating a reaction isn't as simple as wrapping it up in a lumpy wool jumper and a stripy scarf.
There's more than one way to do it, and you need to be able to decide on the best, and the safest, method.

Bunsen Burners Have a Naked Flame

Bunsen burners are good for heating things quickly. You can easily adjust how strongly they're heating. But you need to be careful not to use them if you're heating flammable compounds as the flame means the substance would be at risk of catching fire.

Here's how to use a Bunsen burner...

- Connect the Bunsen burner to a gas tap, and check that the hole is closed. Place it on a heat-proof mat.
- Light a splint and hold it over the Bunsen burner. Now, turn on the gas. The Bunsen burner should light with a yellow flame.
- The more open the hole is, the more strongly the Bunsen burner will heat your substance. Open the hole to the amount you want. As you open the hole more, the flame should turn more blue.
- The hottest part of the flame is just above the blue cone, so you should heat things here.
- If your Bunsen burner is alight but not heating anything, make sure you close the hole so that the flame becomes orange and clearly visible.
- If you're heating something so that the container (e.g. a test tube) is in the flame, you should hold the vessel at the top, furthest away from the substance (and so the flame) using a pair of tongs.
- If you're heating something over the flame (e.g. an evaporating dish), you should put a tripod and gauze over the Bunsen burner before you light it, and place the vessel on this.

You'd use a Bunsen burner to carry out flame tests to identify metal ions in a compound (see page 60). A sample of the compound is placed on a metal wire that you hold just above the cone of a Bunsen burner with a blue flame. The flame should then change colour depending on what metal ion is in the sample.

The Temperature of Water Baths & Electric Heaters Can Be Set

1) A water bath is a container filled with water that can be heated to a specific temperature.

- Set the temperature on the water bath, and allow the water to heat up.
- Place the vessel containing your substance in the water bath using a pair of tongs. The level of the water outside the vessel should be just above the level of the substance inside the vessel. The substance will then be warmed to the same temperature as the water.

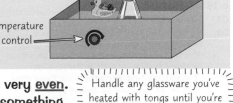

As the substance in the vessel is surrounded by water, the heating is very even. Water boils at 100 °C though, so you can't use a water bath to heat something to a higher temperature than this — the water won't get hot enough.

> Handle any glassware you've heated with tongs until you're sure it's cooled down.

2) Electric heaters are often made up of a metal plate that can be heated to a certain temperature. The vessel containing the substance you want to heat is placed on top of the hot plate. You can heat substances to higher temperatures than you can in a water bath but, as the vessel is only heated from below, you'll usually have to stir the substance inside to make sure it's heated evenly.

A bath and an electric heater — how I spend my January nights...

You know, I used to have a chemistry teacher who'd play power ballads when the Bunsen burners were alight and sway at the front of the class like he was at a gig. You think I made that up, but it's true.

Answers

p.12 — States of Matter

Q1 a) In a solid, the particles are held by strong forces *[1 mark]* in fixed positions in a regular lattice arrangement *[1 mark]*. The particles don't move but vibrate about their positions *[1 mark]*.

b) In a gas, there's almost no force of attraction between the particles *[1 mark]*. The particles move constantly with random motion *[1 mark]*, travel in straight lines and only interact when they collide *[1 mark]*.

c) In a liquid, there are some forces of attraction between the particles *[1 mark]*. The particles move constantly with random motion *[1 mark]* but they do tend to stick to each other *[1 mark]*.

p.13 — The History of the Atom

Q1 The plum pudding model predicted that most of the alpha particles would pass straight through the sheet or be deflected slightly at most *[1 mark]*. In fact, though most of the particles did pass straight through the gold atoms, a few were deflected more than expected and a small number were deflected straight back *[1 mark]*. This suggested that most of the atom is made up of empty space, with a positive nucleus in the centre *[1 mark]*.

Q2 E.g.

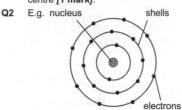

nucleus   shells

electrons

[1 mark for correct structure, 1 mark for correct labels]

p.14 — The Atom

Q1 a) +1

b) 0

c) −1

[1 mark for all three parts correct]

Q2 In the nucleus *[1 mark]*.

Q3 nuclear radius, atomic radius, simple molecule, nanoparticle *[2 marks for all 4 correct, 1 mark if up to 2 are incorrect]*.

p.15 — Atoms, Ions and Isotopes

Q1 a) 16 − 8 = 8 neutrons *[1 mark]*

b) 40 − 20 = 20 neutrons *[1 mark]*

c) 127 − 53 = 74 neutrons *[1 mark]*

Q2 a) Chlorine-35: 17 protons, 17 electrons and (35 − 17 =) 18 neutrons *[1 mark]*.
Chlorine-37: 17 protons, 17 electrons and (37 − 17 =) 20 neutrons *[1 mark]*.

b) 17 + 1 = 18 electrons *[1 mark]*

p.16 — The Periodic Table

Q1 2 *[1 mark]*

Q2 Potassium and sodium are both in Group 1. Potassium and calcium are in different groups. So the chemical properties of potassium should be closer to those of sodium than calcium *[1 mark]*, because elements in the same group have similar chemical properties *[1 mark]*.

p.17 — Electron Shells

Q1 2.8.3 or

[1 mark]

Q2 Group 2 *[1 mark]*
Period 4 *[1 mark]*

p.18 — Ionic Bonding

Q1 Each potassium atom loses an electron to form a K^+ ion *[1 mark]*. Each chlorine atom gains an electron to form a Cl^- ion *[1 mark]*.
The oppositely charged ions are attracted to each other by electrostatic forces to form an ionic bond *[1 mark]*.

p.19 — Ionic Compounds

Q1

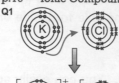

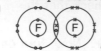

[1 mark for arrow showing electron transferred from potassium to chlorine, 1 mark for correct outer shell electron configurations, 1 mark for correct charges]

Q2 When melted, the ions are free to move, so they can carry an electric current *[1 mark]*.

p.20 — Simple Molecules

Q1

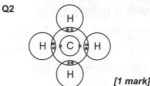

[1 mark]

Q2

H C H with H above and H below

[1 mark]

p.21 — Giant Covalent Structures and Fullerenes

Q1 Similarities: any two from, e.g. giant covalent structure / covalent bonding / high melting point *[1 mark for each similarity]*.
Differences: any two from, e.g. diamond is colourless, graphite is black / graphite conducts electricity, diamond doesn't / carbon atoms form 4 covalent bonds in diamond, and 3 in graphite *[1 mark for each difference]*.

p.22 — Nanoparticles

Q1 Any three from, e.g. catalysts / lubricant coatings / tiny electrical circuits / antibacterial materials / sun creams / deodorants / stronger plastics *[1 mark for each correct use]*.

p.23 — Polymers and Properties of Materials

Q1 The properties of polymers depend on the forces between the chains *[1 mark]*. The properties of polymers A and B suggest that B has only weak intermolecular forces between its chains *[1 mark]*, while it is likely that A has stronger links such as covalent bonds/ cross-links between the chains *[1 mark]*.

p.24 — Metals

Q1 Copper is a good electrical conductor *[1 mark]* as it contains delocalised electrons which are free to move and carry an electrical current *[1 mark]*.

p.25 — States, Structure and Bonding

Q1 a) A — gas *[1 mark]*, B — solid *[1 mark]*, C — liquid *[1 mark]*.

b) A is likely to be a simple molecular structure *[1 mark]*, since simple molecular substances have low melting and boiling points *[1 mark]*. B is likely to be a metal *[1 mark]*, as metals have high melting points and are good electrical conductors *[1 mark]*. D is likely to be ionic *[1 mark]*, as ionic compounds have high melting and boiling points, and conduct electricity when molten, but not when solid *[1 mark]*.

p.26 — Purity

Q1 Under the scientific definition, a pure substance is a substance completely made up of a single element or compound *[1 mark]*. Orange juice is not chemically pure, since it is a mixture (of water, sugars and other compounds) *[1 mark]*.

Q2 Steel has a lower melting point than pure iron *[1 mark]*. The carbon in the iron makes it impure, and impurities lower the melting point *[1 mark]*.

p.27 — Distillation

Q1 Ethanol will be collected in the second fraction *[1 mark]*, because it has the second lowest boiling point of the three compounds in the mixture *[1 mark]*.

p.28 — Filtration and Crystallisation

Q1 Slowly heat the solution to evaporate off some of the water *[1 mark]*. Stop heating once some of the water has evaporated, or once copper sulfate crystals start to form *[1 mark]*. Allow the solution to cool until copper sulfate crystals form *[1 mark]*. Filter the crystals out of the solution and dry them in a warm place / desiccator / drying oven *[1 mark]*.

p.29 — Chromatography

Q1 Chemical A will end up closer to the solvent front than B *[1 mark]*. A is more soluble in the solvent, so it will spend more time dissolved in the mobile phase, and move further up the plate *[1 mark]*.

p.30 — Interpreting Chromatograms

Q1 R_f of Y = distance travelled by Y ÷ distance travelled by solvent front
= 3.6 cm ÷ 6.0 cm *[1 mark]* = 0.60 *[1 mark]*

p.31 — Relative Masses

Q1 M_r of NaCl = 23.0 + 35.5 = 58.5 *[1 mark]*.

Q2 M_r of C_2H_5OH = (2 × C) + (6 × H) + O
= (2 × 12.0) + (6 × 1.0) + 16.0
= 24.0 + 6.0 + 16.0 = 46.0 *[1 mark]*

Q3 M_r of $Cu(NO_3)_2$ = Cu + 2 × (N + (3 × O))
= 63.5 + 2 × (14.0 + (3 × 16.0)) *[1 mark]*
= 63.5 + 2 × (14.0 + 48.0)
= 63.5 + (2 × 62.0)
= 63.5 + 124.0 = 187.5 *[1 mark]*

p.32 — Molecular and Empirical Formulas

Q1 4, 8 and 2 all divide by 2.
4 ÷ 2 = 2, 8 ÷ 2 = 4, 2 ÷ 2 = 1
So the empirical formula of this compound is C_2H_4Cl *[1 mark]*.

p.34 — Conservation of Mass

Q1 M_r(reactants) = $M_r(H_2SO_4)$ + 2 × M_r(NaOH).
= ((2 × 1.0) + 32.1 + (4 × 16.0)) + 2 × (23.0 + 16.0 + 1.0) = 98.1 + (2 × 40.0) = 178.1 *[1 mark]*
M_r(products) = $M_r(Na_2SO_4)$ + 2 × $M_r(H_2O)$
= ((2 × 23.0) + 32.1 + (4 × 16.0)) + 2 × ((2 × 1.0) + 16.0) = 142.1 + (2 × 18.0) = 178.1 *[1 mark]*
M_r(products) = M_r(reactants), so the mass is conserved *[1 mark]*.

p.35 — Chemical Formulas

Q1 a) Br^- *[1 mark]*

b) CO_3^{2-} *[1 mark]*

c) Li^+ *[1 mark]*

d) NO_3^- *[1 mark]*

Q2 $Mg(OH)_2$ *[1 mark]*

p.36 — Chemical Equations

Q1 $2Fe + 3Cl_2 \rightarrow 2FeCl_3$ *[1 mark]*

Q2 a) water → hydrogen + oxygen *[1 mark]*

b) $2H_2O \rightarrow 2H_2 + O_2$
[1 mark for correct reactants and products, 1 mark for a correctly balanced equation]

p.37 — More on Chemical Equations

Q1 $H^+_{(aq)} + OH^-_{(aq)} \rightarrow H_2O_{(l)}$ *[1 mark]*

Q2 $Cl_2 + 2e^- \rightarrow 2Cl^-$
[1 mark for correct reactants and products, 1 mark for a correctly balanced equation]

p.38 — Moles

Q1 moles = mass ÷ M_r = 90 ÷ 18.0 = 5.0 moles *[1 mark]*

Q2 mass = moles × M_r
= 0.200 × 119.0 = 23.8 moles *[1 mark]*

Q3 M_r = mass ÷ moles = 87.0 ÷ 0.500 = 174 *[1 mark]*

p.39 — Calculating Masses

Q1 $M_r(KBr) = 39.1 + 79.9 = 119$
$M_r(Br_2) = 79.9 \times 2 = 159.8$ *[1 mark]*
moles of KBr = mass ÷ M_r
$= 23.8 ÷ 119 = 0.200$ moles *[1 mark]*
From the equation, 2 moles of KBr react to produce 1 mole of Br_2. So 0.200 moles of KBr will produce (0.200 ÷ 2 =) 0.100 moles of Br_2 *[1 mark]*. So mass of Br_2
$= 0.100 \times 159.8 = 16.0$ g *[1 mark]*.

p.40 — More Mole Calculations

Q1 $M_r(N_2) = 2 \times 14.0 = 28.0$
$M_r(H_2) = 2 \times 1.0 = 2.0$ *[1 mark]*
Ratio: $N_2 = 84 ÷ 28.0 = 3.0$
$H_2 = 12 ÷ 2.0 = 6.0$
Divide by the smallest (3) gives a ratio of $N_2 : H_2$ of 1 : 2 *[1 mark]*.
The balanced equation gives a ratio of $N_2 : H_2$ of 1 : 3, so H_2 must be the limiting reactant *[1 mark]*.

p.41 — Endothermic and Exothermic Reactions

Q1 a) exothermic *[1 mark]*

b)

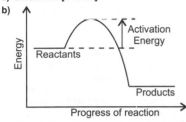

[1 mark for correct shape, 1 mark for correctly labelled axes, 1 mark for correctly labelled products, reactants and activation energy]

p.42 — Bond Energies

Q1 Energy required to break original bonds:
$(1 \times N \equiv N) + (3 \times H–H)$
$= 941 + (3 \times 436) = 941 + 1308$
$= 2249$ kJ/mol *[1 mark]*
Energy released by forming new bonds:
$(6 \times N–H)$
$= 6 \times 391 = 2346$ kJ/mol *[1 mark]*
Overall energy change:
$= 2249 – 2346 = –97$ kJ/mol *[1 mark]*

p.43 — Acids and Bases

Q1 a) Acidic *[1 mark]*

b) Yellow *[1 mark]*

p.44 — Strong and Weak Acids

Q1 A strong acid ionises/dissociates completely in water *[1 mark]*. A weak acid only dissociates a small amount in water *[1 mark]*.

Q2 It increased *[1 mark]* by a factor of 1000 *[1 mark]*.

p.45 — Reactions of Acids

Q1 $2HCl + CaCO_3 \rightarrow CaCl_2 + H_2O + CO_2$
[1 mark for correct reactants and products, 1 mark for a correctly balanced equation]

p.46 — Making Salts

Q1 E.g. React the base, iron oxide, with the acid, nitric acid. Keep on adding base until all the acid has been neutralised — at this point, no more base will react and it will sink to the bottom of the flask *[1 mark]*. Then, filter out the excess solid using filter paper, and collect the solution of salt and water *[1 mark]*. Then, gently evaporate off some of the water from your salt and water solution and leave to allow the salt to crystallise *[1 mark]*.

p.47 — Oxidation and Reduction

Q1 H^+ *[1 mark]*

Q2 positive ions/cations *[1 mark]*

p.48 — Electrolysis

Q1 $2Br^- \rightarrow Br_2 + 2e^-$ *[1 mark]*

p.49 — Electrolysis of Copper Sulfate

Q1 The mass of the anode should decrease *[1 mark]* as copper from the anode decomposes to Cu^{2+} ions in the electrolyte *[1 mark]*.

p.51 — Group 1 — Alkali Metals

Q1 When the alkali metals react, they lose their single outer electron *[1 mark]*. As you go down Group 1, the outer electron gets further from the nucleus *[1 mark]* so less energy is needed to remove it/it is more easily lost *[1 mark]*.

Q2 $2Li + 2H_2O \rightarrow 2LiOH + H_2$
[1 mark for correct reactants and products, 1 mark for correctly balanced equation]

p.52 — Group 7 — Halogens

Q1 Bromine would be a solid at this temperature *[1 mark]*. The melting points of the halogens increase as you go down the group, so at the melting point of chlorine, bromine would still be solid *[1 mark]*.

Q2 $2Na + I_2 \rightarrow 2NaI$
[1 mark for correct reactants and products, 1 mark for correctly balanced equation]

p.53 — Halogen Displacement Reactions

Q1 Bromine water *[1 mark]*.

p.54 — Group 0 — Noble Gases

Q1 Any answer between –130 °C and –93 °C *[1 mark]*.

p.55 — Transition Metals

Q1 E.g. Haber process and iron / Contact process and vanadium pentoxide/V_2O_5 *[1 mark for any industrial process and matching catalyst]*.

Q2 a) Palladium, as in general transition metals have higher densities than Group 1 metals *[1 mark]*.

b) Rubidium, as in general Group 1 metals are more reactive than transition metals *[1 mark]*.

p.56 — Reactivity of Metals

Q1 a) Metal B, Metal C, Metal A *[1 mark]*

b) Metal A is copper. Metal B is magnesium. Metal C is zinc *[1 mark for all three correct]*.

p.57 — The Reactivity Series and Displacement

Q1 Magnesium would displace iron from iron sulfate solution, because it's higher up than iron in the reactivity series/more reactive than iron *[1 mark]*.

Q2 Tin would not displace zinc from zinc sulfate solution, as it's lower than zinc in the reactivity series/it's less reactive than zinc *[1 mark]*.

p.58 — Tests for Gases

Q1 Check to see if the gas will relight a glowing splint *[1 mark]*. If the splint will relight, the gas is oxygen *[1 mark]*.

Q2 Gas A is chlorine *[1 mark]*.
Gas B is hydrogen *[1 mark]*.

p.59 — Tests for Anions

Q1 The solution contains bromide ions *[1 mark]*.

Q2 Add some barium chloride solution to the sample *[1 mark]*. If the solution contains sulfate ions, a white precipitate will form *[1 mark]*. Then add dilute hydrochloric acid *[1 mark]*. If the solution contains sulfate ions, the precipitate should not dissolve *[1 mark]*.

p.60 — Tests for Cations

Q1 The compound contains calcium / Ca^{2+} ions *[1 mark]*.

Q2 The solution contains iron(II) / Fe^{2+} ions *[1 mark]*.

p.61 — Chemical Analysis

Q1 pentane *[1 mark]*

p.63 — Concentration

Q1 200 cm³ $= (200 ÷ 1000)$ dm³ $= 0.2$ dm³ *[1 mark]*
mass = concentration × volume
$= 55 \times 0.2 = 11$ g *[1 mark]*

Q2 First, calculate what mass of solute you need *[1 mark]*. Weigh out this mass of solute in a beaker *[1 mark]*. Add some deionised water to the beaker and stir until all the solute is dissolved *[1 mark]*. Tip the solution into a volumetric flask of the correct size. Rinse the beaker and the stirring rod with deionised water and add the washings to the flask *[1 mark]*. Add more deionised water to the flask until the bottom of the meniscus is on the line *[1 mark]*. Stopper the bottle and turn it upside down a few times to mix the solution, then check the meniscus *[1 mark]*.

p.64 — Titrations

Q1 moles of HCl $= 0.50 \times (27 ÷ 1000)$
$= 0.0135$ moles *[1 mark]*
According to the equation, 1 mole of HCl reacts with 1 mole of NaOH, so 0.0135 moles of HCl must react with 0.0135 moles of NaOH *[1 mark]*.
concentration of NaOH = moles ÷ volume
$= 0.0135 ÷ (15 ÷ 1000) = 0.90$ mol/dm³ *[1 mark]*

p.65 — Calculations with Gases

Q1 moles = mass ÷ A_r
moles of Ar $= 2.349 ÷ 39.9 = 0.060$ mol *[1 mark]*
molar volume = volume ÷ moles
$= 1.32 ÷ 0.060 = 22$ dm³/mol *[1 mark]*

Q2 moles = mass ÷ M_r
moles of $CH_4 = 36 ÷ 16.0 = 2.25$ moles *[1 mark]*
volume = moles × 24 $= 2.25 \times 24$
$= 54$ dm³ *[1 mark]*

p.66 — Percentage Yield

Q1 $(1.2 ÷ 4.0) \times 100 = 30\%$ *[1 mark]*

Q2 $M_r(Ag_2O) = (2 \times 107.9) + 16.0 = 231.8$
$M_r(Ag) = 107.9$
Moles $Ag_2O = 3.477 ÷ 231.8 = 0.015$ mol *[1 mark]*
The equation tells you that 2 moles of Ag_2O form 4 moles of Ag, so 0.015 moles of Ag_2O produce $(0.015 ÷ 2) \times 4 = 0.030$ moles of Ag *[1 mark]*.
Mass of 0.030 moles of Ag $= 0.030 \times 107.9$
$= 3.237$ g *[1 mark]*.
% yield $= (1.62 ÷ 3.237) \times 100 = 50.0\%$ *[1 mark]*

p.67 — Atom Economy

Q1 M_r of all products $= M_r(CO_2) + [2 \times M_r(H_2)]$
$= [12.0 + (2 \times 16.0)] + [2 \times (2 \times 1.0)]$
$= 44.0 + 4.0 = 48.0$ *[1 mark]*
M_r of desired product $= 2 \times M_r(H_2)$
$= 2 \times (2 \times 1.0) = 4.0$ *[1 mark]*
Atom economy $= (4.0 ÷ 48.0) \times 100$
$= 8.3\%$ *[1 mark]*

Q2 Any two from, e.g. to minimise the resources used / to reduce the waste created / to reduce costs of raw materials / to reduce costs of cleaning up waste *[1 mark for each reason]*.

p.68 — Reaction Rates

Q1 E.g. mix the two solutions and place the reaction vessel over a sheet of paper with a mark on it *[1 mark]*. Time how long it takes for the mark to be obscured *[1 mark]*.

Q2 E.g. it releases the gas straight into the room, so if the gas is harmful you'll need to take safety precautions *[1 mark]*.

p.69 — Rate Experiments

Q1 E.g. place a measured volume of hydrochloric acid of a known concentration in a conical flask on a mass balance. Add a known mass of magnesium metal *[1 mark]*. Take readings of the total mass of the flask at regular time intervals *[1 mark]*. Repeat the experiment with the same volume and concentration of acid and the same mass of magnesium. Increase the surface area of the magnesium by cutting it into smaller pieces *[1 mark]*.

p.70 — Calculating Rates

Q1 E.g.

[1 mark]

Change in $y = 23 – 11 = 12$
Change in $x = 45 – 5 = 40$
Gradient $= 12 ÷ 40 = 0.3$ cm³/s *[1 mark]*

p.71 — Collision Theory

Q1 It would be faster with calcium carbonate powder than with calcium carbonate chips *[1 mark]*. The powder has a higher surface area to volume ratio than the chips *[1 mark]*. This means that the frequency of collisions will increase and so the rate will increase *[1 mark]*.

Q2 As the temperature increases, the speed that the particles move at increases, so there are more collisions *[1 mark]*. Higher temperatures also increase the energy of the collisions *[1 mark]*. So at higher temperatures there are more successful collisions / more particles collide with enough energy to react *[1 mark]*.

p.72 — Catalysts

Q1 A catalyst is a substance that increases the speed of reaction *[1 mark]*, without being chemically changed or used up in the reaction *[1 mark]*.

Q2 At the end of the reaction, the same amount of dark brown PbO_2 powder should still be visible at the bottom of the flask *[1 mark]*.

p.73 — Dynamic Equilibrium

Q1 A reversible reaction is one where the products can react with each other to produce the reactants *[1 mark]*.

Q2 Dynamic equilibrium occurs when the forwards and backwards reactions in a reversible reaction occur at the same rate *[1 mark]*.

Q3 Temperature, *[1 mark]* pressure *[1 mark]* and concentration *[1 mark]*.

p.74 — Le Chatelier's Principle

Q1 The position of equilibrium will shift to the right (towards the products) *[1 mark]*. The forward reaction is endothermic, so when the temperature is increased the equilibrium position will move to the right to absorb the excess heat *[1 mark]*.

Q2 Decreasing the pressure would shift the equilibrium position to the left (towards the reactants) *[1 mark]* as there are more fewer moles of gas on the reactant side than on the products side *[1 mark]*. So the yield of SO_3 would decrease *[1 mark]*.

p.76 — Extracting Metals from their Ores

Q1 Tin is less reactive than carbon *[1 mark]* so you could extract tin from its ore by reducing it with carbon *[1 mark]*.

Q2 $2ZnO + C \rightarrow 2Zn + CO_2$
[1 mark for correct reactants and products, 1 mark for balanced equation]

p.77 — Extracting Metals with Electrolysis

Q1

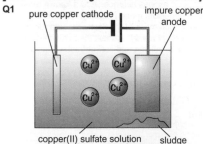

pure copper cathode

impure copper anode

copper(II) sulfate solution   sludge

[1 mark for correct cathode, 1 mark for correct anode, 1 mark for correct labels]

Q2 Bioleaching uses bacteria to separate metals from their ores *[1 mark]*. The bacteria get energy from some of the bonds between the atoms in the metal ore and separate the metal from the ore. The leachate contains the metal ions, which can be extracted (by, e.g. electrolysis or by displacement with a more reactive metal) *[1 mark]*. Phytoextraction involves growing plants in soils that contain metal compounds *[1 mark]*. The metals build up in the plants (since the plant can't use or get rid of them). The plants can be harvested, dried and burnt, and the metal compounds collected from the ash left in the furnace *[1 mark]*.

p.78 — Alloys

Q1 E.g. girders / bridges / engine parts / cutlery / saucepans / ships / drill bits / cars *[1 mark]*.

Q2 E.g. It's strong and very low density / it's light compared to its volume *[1 mark]*.

p.79 — Corrosion

Q1 It creates a barrier that separates the metal from water and oxygen *[1 mark]*.

Q2 Magnesium is more reactive than iron *[1 mark]*, so will lose electrons / be oxidised in preference to iron *[1 mark]*.

p.80 — The Haber Process

Q1 The yield of ammonia would increase *[1 mark]*. A higher pressure would favour the forward reaction/push the position of equilibrium over to the right as there are fewer moles of gas in the products *[1 mark]*.

p.81 — Fertilisers

Q1 Fertilisers replace / provide the essential elements that a plant needs to grow *[1 mark]*.

Q2 Nitrogen, phosphorus and potassium *[2 marks for all three correct, otherwise 1 mark for any two correct answers]*

Q3 Set up titration apparatus by filling a burette with sulfuric acid solution, and clamping it over a conical flask containing ammonia solution *[1 mark]*. Add a few drops of methyl orange indicator *[1 mark]*. Then, slowly add the sulfuric acid until the solution changes from yellow to red *[1 mark]*. Repeat this experiment using identical quantities of nitric acid and ammonia solution, but with no indicator *[1 mark]*. Then, gently evaporate the solution until only a little bit is left and leave to allow ammonium sulfate crystals to form *[1 mark]*. Filter the crystals out of the solution and leave to dry *[1 mark]*.

p.82 — The Contact Process

Q1 $S_{(s)} + O_{2(g)} \rightarrow SO_{2(g)}$
$2SO_{2(g)} + O_{2(g)} \rightleftharpoons 2SO_{3(g)}$
$SO_{3(g)} + H_2O_{(l)} \rightarrow H_2SO_{4(aq)}$
[1 mark for each correct equation, 1 mark correct state symbols in each equation]

Q2 You could increase the pressure *[1 mark]*. Increasing the pressure would move the equilibrium position over to the right / favour the forwards reaction, since there are fewer moles of gas with the products *[1 mark]*.

p.83 — Industrial Processes

Q1 E.g. the availability of the raw materials *[1 mark]* and the cost of the raw materials *[1 mark]*.

p.84 — Life-Cycle Assessments

Q1 Any four from e.g. the energy required to extract the raw materials / whether the raw materials are renewable or not / whether other harmful emissions (e.g. CO/HCl) are produced / whether the waste products are harmful or not / how environmentally friendly the cars are to dispose of *[1 mark for each]*.

p.85 — Recycling Materials

Q1 E.g. Metals are non-renewable, so recycling metals is important to conserve finite resources of the metal *[1 mark]*. Also, non-recycled material has to be disposed of in landfill sites, which take up space and can pollute the surroundings *[1 mark]*.

p.86 — Types of Materials

Q1 Any two from e.g.: clay / glass / porcelain / bone china *[1 mark]*

p.87 — Materials and their Uses

Q1 E.g. polypropylene would be the best choice *[1 mark]*. The flask should be a poor thermal conductor, so that the contents of the flask stay warm, so copper and steel are poor choices *[1 mark]*. Carbon fibre is very expensive, and since the flask does not need to be especially strong, polypropylene is a better choice *[1 mark]*.

p.88 — Alkanes and Alkenes

Q1 $C_4H_{10} + 6\frac{1}{2}O_2 \rightarrow 4CO_2 + 5H_2O$ *[1 mark]*

p.89 — Alcohols

Q1 Propanol *[1 mark]*

Q2 Butanol *[1 mark]*

p.90 — Addition Polymerisation

Q1

$$\left[\begin{array}{cc} Cl & Cl \\ | & | \\ -C & -C- \\ | & | \\ H & H \end{array} \right]_n$$

[1 mark]

p.91 — Condensation Polymers

Q1 A carboxylic acid with two carboxylic acid functional groups (one on each end of the molecule) / a dicarboxylic acid *[1 mark]* and an alcohol with two alcohol functional groups (one on each end of the molecule) / a diol *[1 mark]*.

p.92 — Crude Oil

Q1 LPG, Petrol, Naphtha, Kerosene/Paraffin, Diesel, Oil and Bitumen
[5 marks for all correct and in the correct order, otherwise lose 1 mark for each error]

Q2 Propane and butane *[1 mark]*

p.93 — Hydrocarbons

Q1 Alkane B will have the higher boiling point *[1 mark]* as it has a longer hydrocarbon chain, so has stronger intermolecular forces between the chains *[1 mark]*.

Q2 E.g. generate electricity / as fuel / make chemicals *[1 mark for each correct use]*.

p.94 — Cracking

Q1 Powdered aluminium oxide catalyst *[1 mark]*, 400 °C - 700 °C and 70 atm *[1 mark]*.

Q2 C_9H_{18} *[1 mark]*

p.95 — Fuel Cells

Q1 $2H_2 + O_2 \rightarrow 2H_2O$ *[1 mark]*

Q2 Advantage: e.g. they don't generate pollutants / they're efficient *[1 mark]*.
Disadvantage: e.g. it's expensive to adapt current technology to run off fuel cells / hydrogen as a fuel is expensive to extract and store *[1 mark]*.

p.96 — The Atmosphere

Q1 Nitrogen gas was formed by the reaction between ammonia and oxygen *[1 mark]* and was also released by denitrifying bacteria *[1 mark]*. The proportion of nitrogen in our atmosphere increased because it's unreactive, so it wasn't reacted as it was made *[1 mark]*.

p.97 — The Greenhouse Effect

Q1 Electromagnetic radiation, from the Sun, passes through the atmosphere where it is absorbed. This warms the Earth *[1 mark]*. The Earth gives out some of the heat radiation it absorbs *[1 mark]*. Some of this radiation is re-emitted back into space, but some is absorbed or reflected back to Earth by greenhouse gases *[1 mark]*. This is the greenhouse effect and works to keep the Earth warm.

Q2 E.g. carbon dioxide, water vapour and methane *[1 mark for each]*

p.98 — Global Warming

Q1 Global warming is the increase in the average temperature of the Earth *[1 mark]*. It is caused by the enhanced greenhouse effect / the increase in the proportion of greenhouse gases in the atmosphere *[1 mark]*.

p.99 — Pollutants

Q1 Acid rain forms when nitrogen oxides and sulfur dioxide *[1 mark]*, mix with clouds to form dilute nitric acid and dilute sulfuric acid *[1 mark]*. (This falls as acid rain.)

Q2 E.g. carbon monoxide *[1 mark]*, (carbon) particulates *[1 mark]*.

p.100 — Water Treatment

Q1 Surface water is first filtered through a wire mesh to filter out large impurities, and then through gravel and sand to filter out any further solid impurities *[1 mark]*. Then, a sedimentation process, which involves adding aluminium sulfate or iron sulfate to the water, causes fine particles to clump together and settle at the bottom *[1 mark]*. Finally, chlorine gas is bubbled through the water to kill any microbes or harmful bacteria *[1 mark]*.

Q2 Nitrate residues come from excess fertiliser that is run off into rivers and lakes *[1 mark]*. They're dangerous as, in high quantities, they can cause serious health problems by preventing the blood from carrying oxygen properly *[1 mark]*.

Answers

Index

Index